SCOTT FORESMAN · ADDISON WESLEY

Mathematics

GRADE 3

VIRGINIA

Virginia Daily Practice and SOL Test Prep

Table of Contents

Cover: ©Buddy Mays/Corbis

ISBN: 0-328-10378-0

7 8 9 10 V084 13 12 11 10 09 08 07

Lesson 1-1   Name _____

1 How is the number on the package used?

ⓐ To name   ⓒ To locate
ⓑ To count   ⓓ To measure

2 How are the numbers on the ruler used?

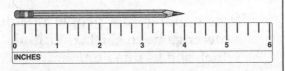

ⓕ To name   ⓗ To locate
ⓖ To count   ⓙ To measure

3 How is the number on the mailbox used?

ⓐ To name   ⓒ To locate
ⓑ To count   ⓓ To measure

4 How is the number on the road sign used?

ⓕ To name
ⓖ To count
ⓗ To locate
ⓙ To measure

5 Virginia was the tenth state to join the Union in 1788. How many states joined before Virginia?

ⓐ 8
ⓑ 9
ⓒ 10
ⓓ 1787

6 What ordinal number comes next?

21st, 22nd, 23rd, _____

ⓕ 20th
ⓖ 24th
ⓗ 26th
ⓙ 29th

Lesson 1-2   Name _____

1 Which number is shown by the place-value blocks?

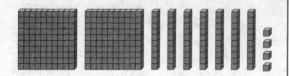

- (A) 247
- (B) 274
- (C) 472
- (D) 742

2 Which number has the same value as 700 + 9?

- (F) 7,009
- (G) 790
- (H) 709
- (J) 79

3 Which number will make this number sentence true?

483 = 400 + ☐ + 3

- (A) 8
- (B) 48
- (C) 80
- (D) 83

4 Bristol, Virginia, is 329 miles away from Norfolk, Virginia. Which shows this number in word form?

- (F) Three, two, nine
- (G) Three, twenty-nine
- (H) Three hundred, twenty
- (J) Three hundred, twenty-nine

5 Which number is the standard form of six hundred fifteen?

- (A) 600,015
- (B) 6,015
- (C) 615
- (D) 6.15

6 Nine hundred four people attended a soccer game in Fairfax, Virginia. Which shows this number in standard form?

- (F) 94
- (G) 904
- (H) 9,004
- (J) 900,400

7 Use the digits 3, 4, and 5 to write as many different 3-digit numbers as you can using each digit only once in each number.

_____

Write the word form for one of your numbers that starts with 4.

_____

2

Lesson 1-3   Name _____

1 Which of the following does not show the number 124?

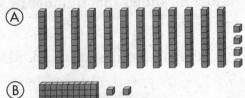

Ⓐ

Ⓑ

Ⓒ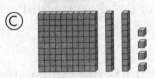

Ⓓ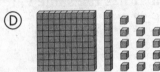

2 The number 850 can be renamed as how many tens?

Ⓕ 5 tens

Ⓖ 50 tens

Ⓗ 85 tens

Ⓙ 800 tens

3 Which number has the same value as 46 tens?

Ⓐ 46

Ⓑ 460

Ⓒ 4,600

Ⓓ 4,610

4 Roanoke, Virginia is 940 feet above sea level. This number can be renamed as how many tens?

Ⓕ 4

Ⓖ 40

Ⓗ 90

Ⓙ 94

5 Which number is shown by the place-value blocks?

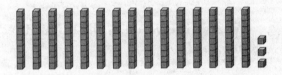

Ⓐ 18

Ⓑ 103

Ⓒ 150

Ⓓ 153

6 Kevin has 23 tens blocks and 8 ones blocks. What other blocks does he need to show 248?

Ⓕ 1 ones block

Ⓖ 1 tens block

Ⓗ 1 hundreds block

Ⓙ 10 tens blocks

Lesson 1-4   Name _____

1 Which number is shown by the place-value blocks?

- Ⓐ 4,321
- Ⓑ 4,231
- Ⓒ 1,324
- Ⓓ 1,234

2 What is the value of the underlined 9 in 6,9̲85?

- Ⓕ 9
- Ⓖ 90
- Ⓗ 900
- Ⓙ 9,000

3 Which number will make this number sentence true?

$$5,000 + 200 + \boxed{} + 8 = 5,238$$

- Ⓐ 23
- Ⓑ 30
- Ⓒ 38
- Ⓓ 52

4 The height of Mount Rogers in Virginia is 5,729 feet. Which of the following shows that number in word form?

- Ⓕ Five thousand, seven hundred
- Ⓖ Five thousand, twenty-nine
- Ⓗ Five thousand, seven, twenty-nine
- Ⓙ Five thousand, seven hundred, twenty-nine

5 Which number has the same value as 6,000 + 40 + 3?

- Ⓐ 643
- Ⓑ 6,043
- Ⓒ 6,403
- Ⓓ 6,430

6 There are 5,280 feet in a mile. Which of the following shows that number in expanded form?

- Ⓕ 5 + 2 + 8 + 0
- Ⓖ 5,000 + 28 + 0
- Ⓗ 5,000 + 2 + 80
- Ⓙ 5,000 + 200 + 80

7 Explain how you know that 3,500 and 3,050 do not name the same number.

_____

_____

Lesson 1-5   Name _____

1 Which shows 240,705 written in expanded form?

Ⓐ 2 + 4 + 7 + 5

Ⓑ 240 + 705

Ⓒ 200,000 + 40,000 + 7,000 + 5

Ⓓ 200,000 + 40,000 + 700 + 5

2 Which shows 600,000 + 40,000 + 200 + 8 written in standard form?

Ⓕ 642,800

Ⓖ 640,208

Ⓗ 640,028

Ⓙ 6,428

3 Which number has the same value as 50,000 + 800 + 70 + 8?

Ⓐ 508,708

Ⓑ 58,708

Ⓒ 50,878

Ⓓ 5,878

4 What is the value of the underlined 5 in 3<u>5</u>9,623?

Ⓕ 50

Ⓖ 500

Ⓗ 5,000

Ⓙ 50,000

5 In 2000, the population of Norfolk was 234,403. Which of the following shows the population number in word form?

Ⓐ Two hundred thirty-four, four hundred three

Ⓑ Two hundred thousand, thirty-four, four hundred three

Ⓒ Two hundred thirty-four thousand, four hundred three

Ⓓ Four hundred three thousand, two hundred thirty-four

6 Which number will make this number sentence true?

$$46{,}020 = 40{,}000 + \boxed{} + 20$$

Ⓕ 6

Ⓖ 60

Ⓗ 600

Ⓙ 6,000

7 Forty-five thousand, forty-nine people were counted in Charlottesville for the 2000 census. Which of the following shows the population in standard form?

Ⓐ 40,549

Ⓑ 45,049

Ⓒ 45,409

Ⓓ 49,045

Lesson 1-6   Name _____

1 Ben read 9 books in January, 6 books in February, and 7 books in March. How many books did he read in February and March?

ⓐ 22

ⓑ 16

ⓒ 15

ⓓ 13

2 Maria had 15 Canadian stamps and 23 Mexican stamps. She gave 8 Mexican and 9 Canadian stamps to her friend. How many stamps did she give to her friend?

ⓕ 14

ⓖ 17

ⓗ 38

ⓙ 55

3 Abdul's scout troop went on a hike to look for birds. They saw 25 cardinals, 20 robins, and 50 crows. How many more crows did they see than robins?

ⓐ 25

ⓑ 30

ⓒ 45

ⓓ 70

4 The Davis family traveled from Richmond to Newport News. From there they plan to drive to Virginia Beach through Norfolk. How many more miles will they have to travel to get to Virginia Beach?

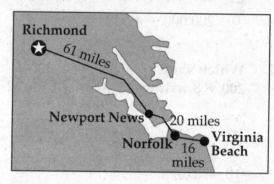

ⓕ 16

ⓖ 36

ⓗ 80

ⓙ 97

5 What is the total distance in miles they will travel?

ⓐ 61

ⓑ 77

ⓒ 81

ⓓ 97

6 A third-grade class is collecting cans of food for a food drive. They have already collected 30 cans of soup, 40 cans of fruit, and 25 cans of vegetables. How many cans of fruit and vegetables have they collected?

_____

What are the key facts you used to find the answer?

_____

Lesson 1-7   Name _____

1   **Which number sentence is true?**

Ⓐ   588 > 688

Ⓑ   209 > 199

Ⓒ   456 > 457

Ⓓ   733 > 803

2   **The distance from Roanoke, Virginia to Marietta, Georgia, is 345 miles. Which number is LESS THAN that number?**

Ⓕ   354

Ⓖ   344

Ⓗ   345

Ⓙ   347

3   **Which number will make this number sentence true?**

4,298 > _____

Ⓐ   4,829

Ⓑ   4,289

Ⓒ   5,008

Ⓓ   5,209

4   **Which symbol will make this number sentence true?**

2,798 ☐ 2,978

Ⓕ   <

Ⓖ   >

Ⓗ   =

Ⓙ   +

Use the table for 5–7.

City	Height Above Sea Level (feet)
Charlottesville	594
Danville	500
Roanoke	940
Winchester	720

5   **The table gives the heights of four cities in Virginia in feet above sea level. Which city in the table has a height GREATER THAN Winchester?**

Ⓕ   Charlottesville

Ⓖ   Danville

Ⓗ   Roanoke

Ⓙ   Winchester

6   **Which city in the table has the lowest height above sea level?**

Ⓐ   Charlottesville

Ⓑ   Danville

Ⓒ   Roanoke

Ⓓ   Winchester

7   **Which number sentence shows how the heights above sea level compare for Charlottesville and Roanoke?**

Ⓕ   594 > 940

Ⓖ   594 < 720

Ⓗ   940 < 720

Ⓙ   940 > 594

Lesson 1-8 Name _____

1 Which shows the numbers in order from least to greatest?

(A) 2,393   2,339   2,933

(B) 2,339   2,393   2,933

(C) 2,933   2,339   2,393

(D) 2,933   2,393   2,339

2 Which of these numbers has the greatest value?

(F) 8,406

(G) 8,640

(H) 8,460

(J) 8,509

3 Which number will put this set of numbers in order from greatest to least?

875 _____ 857

(A) 855

(B) 866

(C) 877

(D) 888

Use the table for 4 and 5.

Mountain	Height (feet)
Black Mountain, KY	4,145
Clingmans Dome, TN	6,643
Mt. Marcy , NY	5,344
Mount Rogers, VA	5,729

4 The table gives the heights of four mountains and the states they are located in. Which mountain is the tallest?

(F) Black Mountain

(G) Clingmans Dome

(H) Mt. Marcy

(J) Mount Rogers

5 Which mountain in the table is shorter than Mt. Marcy?

(A) Black Mountain

(B) Clingmans Dome

(C) Mt. Marcy

(D) Mount Rogers

6 Katy rolled these 3 numbers. She used them to make as many 3-digit numbers as possible.

How many numbers did she make? _____

List the numbers in order from least to greatest in value.

_____

SOL 3.8 The student will solve problems involving … two whole numbers, each 9,999 or less … using various computational methods…. SOL 3.24 The student will recognize and describe a variety of patterns formed using … numbers [and] tables … and extend the pattern…. SOL 3.25a The student will investigate … patterns involving numbers….

Lesson 1-9   Name _____

1 If the pattern continues, what is the next number?

8, 13, 18, 23, _____

Ⓐ 25

Ⓑ 28

Ⓒ 30

Ⓓ 33

2 What is the pattern used for these numbers?

50, 45, 40, 35, ….

Ⓕ Add 4

Ⓖ Add 5

Ⓗ Subtract 4

Ⓙ Subtract 5

3 Janet puts her flag stickers in an album, using a pattern.

Page 1: 5 stickers

Page 2: 6 stickers

Page 3: 5 stickers

Page 4: 6 stickers

Page 5: 5 stickers

Page 6: 6 stickers

If she continues the pattern, how many stickers will be on Page 9?

Ⓐ 5 stickers

Ⓑ 6 stickers

Ⓒ 28 stickers

Ⓓ 35 stickers

4 Alberto is creating a number pattern. He says each number is four more than the number before it.

15, 19, 23, 27, _____, _____

Which are the next two numbers in his pattern?

Ⓕ 28, 32

Ⓖ 30, 34

Ⓗ 31, 35

Ⓙ 29, 33

5 What is the pattern for these numbers?

95, 85, 75, 65, ….

Ⓐ Add 5

Ⓑ Subtract 5

Ⓒ Add 10

Ⓓ Subtract 10

6 Andrew did 3 sit-ups on Monday, 6 sit-ups on Tuesday, and 9 sit-ups on Wednesday. If Andrew continues in this pattern, how many sit-ups will he do on Friday?

Ⓕ 12

Ⓖ 15

Ⓗ 18

Ⓙ 21

Lesson 1-10   Name _____

1 The distance from Winchester, Virginia to Danville, Virginia is 226 miles. What is 226 rounded to the nearest hundred?

- (A) 200
- (B) 220
- (C) 230
- (D) 300

2 On Sunday, Rosa traveled 85 miles to her grandmother's house. How many miles did she travel, rounded to the nearest ten?

- (F) 70
- (G) 80
- (H) 90
- (J) 100

3 When rounding 4,527 to the nearest thousand, which digit tells you how you should round?

- (A) 2
- (B) 4
- (C) 5
- (D) 7

4 There are 653 people on the beach. What is that number rounded to the nearest ten?

- (F) 50
- (G) 600
- (H) 650
- (J) 660

5 There are 342 buttons in a jar. What is that number rounded to the nearest hundred?

- (A) 300
- (B) 340
- (C) 350
- (D) 400

6 Use the time line to answer the question.

1867: Typewriter invented

1840 1850 1860 1870 1880 1890 1900

The typewriter was invented closer to which year?

- (F) 1860
- (G) 1870
- (H) 1880
- (J) 1900

7 In 2004, Josh said the typewriter was invented 137 years ago. Rounded to the nearest ten, how many years is that?

- (A) 100
- (B) 130
- (C) 140
- (D) 150

Lesson 1-11   Name _____

1   Nicole is making a beaded bracelet.

If her pattern continues, how many beads should come next and in what color?

Ⓐ   2 black beads

Ⓑ   3 black beads

Ⓒ   4 white beads

Ⓓ   4 black beads

2   How many ■ will be in the next figure?

Ⓕ   3

Ⓖ   4

Ⓗ   5

Ⓙ   6

3   Brian made a pyramid of blocks. He used 5 blocks in the bottom row. All the rows are stacked on top of each other. Each row has one less than the row it sits on. How many blocks did Brian use to build his pyramid?

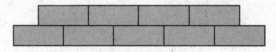

Ⓐ   10

Ⓑ   12

Ⓒ   15

Ⓓ   18

4   Leilani is making a beaded necklace.

If her pattern continues until there are 7 white beads, what is the total number of beads needed to make the necklace?

Ⓕ   12

Ⓖ   21

Ⓗ   28

Ⓙ   35

5   Steven drew a pattern with one square, one triangle, one square, two triangles, one square, three triangles.

Draw this pattern. _____

Draw the next 5 figures in his pattern.

_____

Lesson 1-12   Name _____

1 **Marty has this money in his wallet. How much money does he have?**

(A) $3.04

(B) $3.60

(C) $3.65

(D) $3.75

2 **Kelly has 2 one-dollar bills, 3 quarters, 1 dime, and 5 pennies. How much money does she have?**

(F) $2.75

(G) $2.90

(H) $3.00

(J) $3.10

3 **Which is a way to show $3.40?**

(A) 2 one-dollar bills, 5 quarters, 1 dime, 1 nickel

(B) 3 one-dollar bills, 3 dimes, 10 nickels

(C) 3 one-dollar bills, 6 nickels, 5 pennies

(D) 3 one-dollar bills, 2 quarters, 1 nickel

4 **Brenda used 8 coins to make $0.95. What coins did she use?**

(F) 3 quarters, 2 dimes

(G) 3 quarters, 5 nickels

(H) 2 quarters, 3 dimes, 3 nickels

(J) 2 quarters, 4 dimes, 2 nickels

5 **Leo had this money to spend at the Lynchburg Fair for a snack.**

Which snack costs exactly the same as the value of Leo's money?

(A)  $1.95

(B)  $2.45

(C)  $2.75

(D)  $2.55

12

Lesson 1-13   Name _____

1   Alex bought a book at the Danville Bookstore for $4.35 and gave the clerk a $5 bill. How much change did he get back?

Ⓐ

Ⓑ

Ⓒ

Ⓓ

2   Sheila bought a juice drink that cost $1.69. She gave the clerk two $1 bills. How much change did she get back?

Ⓕ $0.31

Ⓖ $0.41

Ⓗ $1.31

Ⓙ $1.41

3   Kevin bought a seashell for $0.58 when he was in Virginia Beach and paid for it with 3 quarters. How much change did he get back?

Ⓐ $2.42   Ⓒ $0.27

Ⓑ $1.42   Ⓓ $0.17

4   Marsha bought a scarf that cost $3.78. She gave the clerk four $1 bills. How much change did she get back?

Ⓕ   2 dimes, 2 pennies

Ⓖ   1 quarter, 2 pennies

Ⓗ   3 dimes, 2 pennies

Ⓙ   4 dimes, 2 pennies

5   Gary bought an item in the Woodville Elementary School Store with a $5 bill. He got back $1.40 in change. Which item did he buy?

Ⓐ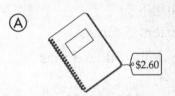
$2.60

Ⓑ
$1.40

Ⓒ
$4.60

Ⓓ
$3.60

13

Lesson 1-14   Name _____

1 How many nickels have the same value as 3 quarters?

(A) 5 nickels   (C) 15 nickels

(B) 10 nickels   (D) 25 nickels

2 Jennie found this money on her dresser. Which amount is more money than Jennie found?

(F) 4 quarters, 7 nickels

(G) 6 quarters

(H) 5 quarters, 5 dimes

(J) 1 one-dollar bill, 6 dimes

3 Bob has 3 sandwiches. He cuts 2 sandwiches into 4 pieces each and one sandwich into 2 pieces. How many pieces of sandwich does he have?

(A) 12   (C) 8

(B) 10   (D) 6

4 The table shows how much money Cathy can earn babysitting. If the pattern continues, how much money can she earn babysitting for 7 hours?

Hours	Pay
1	$3
2	$6
3	$9
4	$12

(F) $15

(G) $18

(H) $21

(J) $24

5 Each time Kyle buys 2 pizzas he can get 1 free drink. Which statement is true?

(A) Kyle can get his 3rd free drink when he buys his 4th pizza.

(B) Kyle can get his 4th free drink when he buys his 6th pizza.

(C) Kyle can get his 4th free drink when he buys his 8th pizza.

(D) Kyle can get his 5th free drink when he buys his 9th pizza.

6 Allen bought an *I ♥ Virginia* T-shirt for $3.65 and paid with a $5 bill. How much change did he get?

_____

Write or draw the change using the least number of bills and coins.

SOL 3.1 The student will read ... six-digit numerals and identify the place value for each digit.
SOL 3.2 The student will round a whole number, 9,999 or less, to the nearest ten....
SOL 3.3 The student will compare two numbers between 0 and 9,999, using symbols (>, <, or =)....

Lesson 1-15   Name _____

1 In 2000, one hundred twenty-eight thousand, two hundred eighty-three people were counted for the census in Alexandria. Which of the following shows the population in standard form?

- Ⓐ 128,000,283
- Ⓑ 128,200,083
- Ⓒ 128,283
- Ⓓ 128,083

2 In 2000, there were 3,522 people in Richmond over 85 years old. Round the number of people to the nearest hundred.

- Ⓕ 3,500
- Ⓖ 3,520
- Ⓗ 3,530
- Ⓙ 3,600

3 The distance from Roanoke, Virginia to Denver, Colorado is 1,548 miles. Which number is LESS THAN that number?

- Ⓐ 1,555
- Ⓑ 1,584
- Ⓒ 1,458
- Ⓓ 1,548

Use the table for 4–6.

College	Votes
George Mason University	1,700
University of Richmond	1,352
University of Virginia	1,902
Virginia Tech University	1,402

4 The table shows results from a vote taken on favorite Virginia colleges. Which college got the most votes?

- Ⓕ George Mason University
- Ⓖ University of Richmond
- Ⓗ University of Virginia
- Ⓙ Virginia Tech University

5 Round the number of votes for the University of Richmond to the nearest ten.

- Ⓐ 1,300
- Ⓒ 1,360
- Ⓑ 1,350
- Ⓓ 1,400

6 Which of the following show the number of votes for University of Virginia in word form?

- Ⓕ One thousand, four hundred, two
- Ⓖ One thousand, nine hundred, twenty
- Ⓗ One hundred nine thousand, two
- Ⓙ One thousand, nine hundred, two

15

Lesson 2-1　　Name _____

1 What number goes in the box to make a true statement?

$$5 + 8 = 8 + \boxed{}$$

- Ⓐ 3
- Ⓑ 5
- Ⓒ 8
- Ⓓ 13

2 The sum of any number and zero is _____.

- Ⓕ Zero
- Ⓖ Ten
- Ⓗ Ten more than the number
- Ⓙ That same number

3 What number goes in the box to make a true statement?

$$(\boxed{} + 3) + 2 = 5 + (3 + 2)$$

- Ⓐ 2
- Ⓑ 3
- Ⓒ 5
- Ⓓ 10

4 Which property is shown by this number sentence?

$$7 + 8 = 8 + 7$$

- Ⓕ Addition (fact) property
- Ⓖ Associative (grouping) property
- Ⓗ Commutative (order) property
- Ⓙ Identity (zero) property

5 Which is a true number sentence?

- Ⓐ $2 + 3 = 5 + 2$
- Ⓑ $4 + 0 = 0$
- Ⓒ $(2 + 7) + 3 = (3 + 7) + 0$
- Ⓓ $6 + 8 = 8 + 6 + 0$

6 What number goes in the box to make a true statement?

$$\boxed{} + 9 = 9$$

- Ⓕ 0
- Ⓖ 1
- Ⓗ 9
- Ⓙ 18

7 Michael is a quarterback on a Danville football team. He threw a pass for a touchdown to score 6 points. Later he threw another pass, but it went out of bounds for no score. How many points did he score?

- Ⓐ 0
- Ⓑ 6
- Ⓒ 7
- Ⓓ 12

8 Which number makes this number sentence true?

$$425 + 0 = \underline{\hspace{1cm}}$$

- Ⓕ 425
- Ⓖ 4,250
- Ⓗ 4,025
- Ⓙ 4,205

Lesson 2-2   Name _____

1 Which number sentence is in the same fact family as 9 + 4 = 13?

   Ⓐ 9 − 4 = 5

   Ⓑ 8 + 5 = 13

   Ⓒ 13 − 9 = 4

   Ⓓ 13 + 4 = 9

2 Find the missing fact for this fact family.

$$8 + 6 = 14$$
$$14 - 8 = 6$$
$$6 + 8 = 14$$

   Ⓕ 8 − 6 = 2

   Ⓖ 5 + 9 = 14

   Ⓗ 14 − 7 = 7

   Ⓙ 14 − 6 = 8

3 Which number sentence is NOT a part of the fact family 7 + 9 = 16?

   Ⓐ 16 − 7 = 9

   Ⓑ 8 + 8 = 16

   Ⓒ 9 + 7 = 16

   Ⓓ 16 − 9 = 7

4 Which number fact is NOT in the same fact family as 7 + 0 = 7?

   Ⓕ 7 − 0 = 7

   Ⓖ 0 − 7 = 7

   Ⓗ 0 + 7 = 7

   Ⓙ 7 + 0 = 7

5 Sarah can use the fact 5 + 8 = 13 to help her solve a related problem. Which of the following could be the problem she is trying to solve?

   Ⓐ 8 − 5 = ▢

   Ⓑ 13 − 8 = ▢

   Ⓒ 13 + 5 = ▢

   Ⓓ ▢ + 5 = 8

6 The basic fact 7 + 5 = 12 is related to the fact _____ in the same fact family.

   Ⓕ 12 − 7 = 5

   Ⓖ 7 − 5 = 2

   Ⓗ 7 + 2 = 9

   Ⓙ 12 − 6 = 6

7 Write a fact family for the numbers 3, 6, and 9.

_____

_____

Write a fact family for the numbers 3, 3, and 6.

_____

_____

Lesson 2-3   Name _____

1 What is the missing number in this table?

In	4	7	5	3	9
Out	9	12	10	8	?

Ⓐ 5

Ⓑ 6

Ⓒ 11

Ⓓ 14

2 What number pattern do you see in this table?

In	4	6	7	9	10
Out	11	13	14	16	17

Ⓕ Add 4

Ⓖ Subtract 4

Ⓗ Add 7

Ⓙ Subtract 7

3 Joshua uses the rule "Add 6" for his table. If he puts in a zero, what number should he get out?

Ⓐ 0

Ⓑ 6

Ⓒ 12

Ⓓ 60

4 Ken used the rule "Add 5" to make this table. What are the missing "Out" numbers?

In	9	7	5	8	11
Out	?	?	?	?	?

Ⓕ 4, 2, 0, 3, 6

Ⓖ 5, 10, 15, 20, 25

Ⓗ 14, 12, 10, 13, 16

Ⓙ 14, 19, 24, 29, 34

5 Which pair of numbers could be used to complete this table?

In	7	9	5	11	?
Out	4	6	2	8	?

Ⓐ In 10, Out 13

Ⓑ In 15, Out 12

Ⓒ In 7, Out 10

Ⓓ In 14, Out 10

6 What rule is used in this table?

In	13	15	18	9	17
Out	9	11	14	5	13

Ⓕ Add 4

Ⓖ Subtract 4

Ⓗ Add 3

Ⓙ Subtract 5

Lesson 2-4   Name _____

1 Which of the following number sentences can be used to find how many more cardinals than owls?

Ⓐ 12 + 5 = ☐

Ⓑ 12 − 5 = ☐

Ⓒ 12 − 17 = ☐

Ⓓ 12 + ☐ = 5

2 Which of the following number sentences can be used to solve this problem? Use the letter *m* to show what you are trying to find.

> Ashley had $9. She earned $7 walking the neighbor's dog. How much money does she have now?

Ⓕ 7 + m = 9   Ⓗ m − 9 = 7

Ⓖ 9 − 7 = m   Ⓙ 9 + 7 = m

3 Brad had a dozen match cars. He sold 5 of them at his family's garage sale. Which number sentence shows how Brad found the number left?

Ⓐ 12 + 5 = 17 match cars left

Ⓑ 10 − 5 = 5 match cars left

Ⓒ 12 − 5 = 7 match cars left

Ⓓ 12 − 7 = 5 match cars left

4 Matthew had 8 Virginia bumper stickers in his collection. He bought 5 more bumper stickers. How many bumper stickers does he have?

Ⓕ 3

Ⓖ 5

Ⓗ 8

Ⓙ 13

5 Mark has 5 quarters, 11 pennies, and 6 dimes in his pocket. How many more pennies does he have than dimes?

Ⓐ 5

Ⓑ 6

Ⓒ 17

Ⓓ 22

6 There are 6 dogwood trees around an elementary school in Harrisonburg. The third-grade class is going to plant 4 more dogwood trees. How many dogwood trees will there be around the school?

Write a number sentence to solve the problem. _____
Use the number sentence to solve the problem. Show your work.

Lesson 2-5   Name _____

1 Which of the following shows 56 written in expanded notation?

   Ⓐ   5 + 6

   Ⓑ   55 + 1

   Ⓒ   50 + 6

   Ⓓ   60 − 4

2 To break apart the number 63 into tens and ones, which two numbers would be best to use when adding mentally to find 63 + 50?

   Ⓕ   6 and 3

   Ⓖ   60 and 3

   Ⓗ   60 and 13

   Ⓙ   40 and 23

3 Which of the following shows a way to break apart numbers in order to add 43 + 36 mentally?

   Ⓐ   40 + 3 and 30 + 6

   Ⓑ   40 + 40 and 30 + 6

   Ⓒ   40 + 30 and 30 + 60

   Ⓓ   4 + 3 and 3 + 6

4 To add 45 + 24 mentally, Jeff thought, "40 + 20 = 60." What should he do next?

   Ⓕ   Add 60 and 24

   Ⓖ   Add 40 and 24

   Ⓗ   Add 20 and 45

   Ⓙ   Add 5 + 4

Use the table for 5–7.

Cities in Virginia	Miles Apart
Richmond to Charlottesville	65
Richmond to Chesapeake	87
Richmond to Williamsburg	46
Williamsburg to Portsmouth	33

5 The table gives the distances in miles between some cities in Virginia. Add mentally to find the total distance from Richmond to Williamsburg to Portsmouth.

   Ⓐ   70 miles

   Ⓑ   79 miles

   Ⓒ   80 miles

   Ⓓ   89 miles

6 Which of the following ways could you use to find the total distance from Charlottesville to Richmond to Williamsburg?

   Ⓕ   60 + 50

   Ⓖ   70 + 50

   Ⓗ   60 + 50 and 5 + 6

   Ⓙ   60 + 40 and 5 + 6

7 From Chesapeake to Richmond to Charlottesville is —

   Ⓐ   142 miles

   Ⓑ   152 miles

   Ⓒ   160 miles

   Ⓓ   162 miles

Lesson 2-6   Name _____

1 Which of the following shows how to find 38 + 7 by breaking up only one of the numbers?

Ⓐ (3 + 8) + 7

Ⓑ 38 + (2 + 5)

Ⓒ (3 + 8) + (2 + 5)

Ⓓ 40 + (10 − 3)

2 Which of the following shows how to "make a ten" to find 38 + 25 mentally?

Ⓕ 30 + (8 + 2) + 5

Ⓖ 3 + (8 + 2) + 5

Ⓗ 30 + 20 + 10 + 5

Ⓙ (38 + 2) + 23

3 Which number will make this number sentence true?

43 + 9 = (43 + 10) − ☐

Ⓐ 9

Ⓑ 3

Ⓒ 2

Ⓓ 1

4 Use mental math. Find 48 + 26.

Ⓕ 22

Ⓖ 60

Ⓗ 74

Ⓙ 80

5 When finding 25 + 57 using mental math, which is an easy way to break apart 25?

Ⓐ 20 + 5

Ⓑ 21 + 4

Ⓒ 22 + 3

Ⓓ 15 + 10

6 Find the sum using mental math.

76 + 9 = ☐

Ⓕ 85

Ⓖ 87

Ⓗ 90

Ⓙ 769

7 Chris said, "To find 55 + 28, I can do 55 + 30, and then _____."

Ⓐ Add 2

Ⓑ Subtract 2

Ⓒ Add 8

Ⓓ Subtract 8

8 Jenny spent $37 at the computer store and $19 at the bookstore. Use mental math to find the amount she spent.

Ⓕ $46

Ⓖ $50

Ⓗ $56

Ⓙ $60

Lesson 2-7   Name _____

1 What is a reasonable estimate for 277 + 85?

  Ⓐ 300

  Ⓑ 400

  Ⓒ 500

  Ⓓ 1,000

2 Which of the following uses front-end estimation to estimate 472 + 327?

  Ⓕ 400 + 300

  Ⓖ 400 + 400

  Ⓗ 500 + 300

  Ⓙ 500 + 400

3 Which of the following uses compatible numbers to estimate 472 + 327?

  Ⓐ 400 + 300

  Ⓑ 500 + 300

  Ⓒ 472 + (8 + 319)

  Ⓓ 475 + 325

Use the map for 4 and 5.

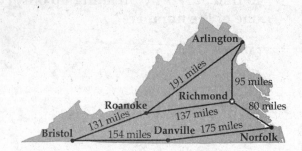

4 Amy's family will drive from Bristol to Richmond, going through Roanoke. Round each number to the nearest ten to estimate the total distance.

  Ⓕ 200 miles

  Ⓖ 260 miles

  Ⓗ 270 miles

  Ⓙ 300 miles

5 Mr. Barker drove from Arlington to Roanoke, going through Richmond. Round each number to the nearest ten to estimate the total distance.

  Ⓐ 190 miles

  Ⓑ 220 miles

  Ⓒ 230 miles

  Ⓓ 240 miles

6 On Thursday, Kim sold 329 apples. On Friday, he sold 284 apples. Estimate the number of apples Kim sold in two days. Write your estimate. Show or explain how you made your estimate.

Estimate: _____

_____

_____

Lesson 2-8   Name _____

1 Paul estimated each sum by rounding. Which estimate is an underestimate?

   (A) 48 + 26 is about 80

   (B) 32 + 91 is about 120

   (C) 247 + 39 is about 290

   (D) 387 + 296 is about 700

2 Kelly said, "56 + 32 is about 90." Which of the following is true about Kelly's statement?

   (F) Kelly found the exact sum.

   (G) Kelly underestimated.

   (H) Kelly overestimated.

   (J) Kelly used compatible numbers to find the answer.

3 Brittany has $70. She wants to buy a jacket for $49, a blouse for $27, and a skirt for $38. She has enough money to buy —

   (A) all three items

   (B) a jacket and a skirt

   (C) a jacket and a blouse

   (D) a skirt and a blouse

4 Which of the following will give an underestimate of 65 + 37?

   (F) 70 + 40

   (G) 65 + 40

   (H) 70 + 37

   (J) 60 + 37

5 The Blue Ridge gift shop had 287 cardinal sweatshirts and 369 flowering dogwood sweatshirts. Estimate the number of sweatshirts in all and tell whether it is an overestimate or underestimate.

   (A) 500, overestimate

   (B) 400, underestimate

   (C) 700, underestimate

   (D) 700, overestimate

6 The shop also had 398 maps of Shenandoah National Park and 576 maps of the Shenandoah Valley. Estimate the number of maps in all and tell whether it is an overestimate or underestimate.

   (F) 800, overestimate

   (G) 900, overestimate

   (H) 1,000, overestimate

   (J) 1,000, underestimate

7 You have $25. You want to buy a CD for $10.99, a cap for $6.29 and a video for $18.99, but can only buy two of the three items. Which items do you buy?

Answer: _____, _____

Show or explain how you decided which two items to buy.

_____

_____

Lesson 2-9   Name _____

1 **Find the difference using mental math.**

$$85 - 39$$

(A) 40

(B) 44

(C) 45

(D) 46

2 **Which of the following shows how to use tens to find 72 − 16 mentally?**

(F) $(70 - 16) + 4$

(G) $(72 - 20) - 4$

(H) $76 - 20$

(J) $70 - 20$

3 **Which of the following shows how to use tens another way to find 72 − 16 mentally?**

(A) $(72 - 20) + 4$

(B) $(72 - 20) - 4$

(C) $(72 - 12) + 10$

(D) $70 - 20$

4 **Ed said, "To find 52 − 27, I can add 3 to 27 to get 52 − 30 = 22, and then _____."**

(F) Subtract 3 from 22

(G) Add 3 to 22

(H) Add 2 to 22

(J) Subtract 2 from 22

Use the table for 5 and 6.

Cities in Virginia	Miles Apart
Richmond to Charlottesville	65
Richmond to Chesapeake	87
Richmond to Williamsburg	46
Richmond to Alexandria	92

5 **The table gives the distances in miles between Richmond and four cities in Virginia. Subtract mentally to find how much farther Alexandria is from Richmond than Charlottesville is from Richmond.**

(A) 5 miles

(B) 27 miles

(C) 46 miles

(D) 157 miles

6 **Which of the following ways could you use to find how much farther it is from Charlottesville to Richmond than from Richmond to Williamsburg?**

(F) $(65 - 50) - 4$

(G) $(65 - 50) + 4$

(H) $(65 - 45) + 1$

(J) $70 - 50$

7 **Find 84 − 57 using mental math.**

(A) 20

(B) 27

(C) 30

(D) 37

Lesson 2-10   Name _____

1 There are 95 counties in Virginia. Jack has been to 62 of them. Which way can Jack count on to find how many counties he still has to visit?

Ⓐ "10, 20, 30, 40, 50, 60, 61, 62 That's 60 + 2, or 62."

Ⓑ "63, 73, 83, 93, 94, 95 That's 30 + 2, or 32."

Ⓒ "62, 63, 64, 65, 75, 85, 95 That's 3 + 30, or 33."

Ⓓ "95, 85, 75, 65, 64, 63 That's 30 + 2, or 32."

2 There are 42 children going on a field trip. There are 28 children already on the bus. How many children need to get on the bus?

Ⓕ 12

Ⓖ 14

Ⓗ 24

Ⓙ 70

3 Use mental math to find the difference.

50 − 27

Ⓐ 23

Ⓑ 33

Ⓒ 37

Ⓓ 87

4 Jamie made 36 bracelets. She needs 75 altogether. How many more does she need to make?

Ⓕ 29

Ⓖ 34

Ⓗ 39

Ⓙ 111

5 Mark gave the cashier $80 to pay for a new jacket. The cashier gave him $16 change. How much did the jacket cost? Use mental math.

Ⓐ $54

Ⓑ $64

Ⓒ $74

Ⓓ $96

6 To find 70 − 28 mentally, Lana thinks:

28 + 2 = 30 and 30 + 40 = 70

All I have to do now is —

Ⓕ add 28 + 30 to get 58 as the answer

Ⓖ add 2 + 30 to get 32 as the answer

Ⓗ add 2 + 40 to get 42 as the answer

Ⓙ add 28 + 30 and then subtract 2 to get 56 as the answer

Lesson 2-11   Name _____

1   Which is the BEST estimate for 487 − 132 if you round the numbers to the nearest ten?

    Ⓐ   About 300

    Ⓑ   About 360

    Ⓒ   About 400

    Ⓓ   About 620

2   Which is the BEST estimate for 619 − 267 if you round the numbers to the nearest hundred?

    Ⓕ   About 200

    Ⓖ   About 300

    Ⓗ   About 400

    Ⓙ   About 900

3   Use front-end estimation to estimate 435 − 178.

    Ⓐ   About 200

    Ⓑ   About 300

    Ⓒ   About 400

    Ⓓ   About 500

4   Estimate. Which two numbers have a difference of about 400?

    Ⓕ   182 and 217

    Ⓖ   112 and 546

    Ⓗ   132 and 591

    Ⓙ   235 and 609

Use the table for 5 and 6.

Grade	Number of Cans Collected
Grade 2	245
Grade 3	409
Grade 4	172
Grade 5	317

5   The table shows the number of tin cans that were collected in one week for the Great Clean Up Week in Pulaski. Using estimation, about how many more cans did the third-grade class collect than the fourth-grade class?

    Ⓐ   70

    Ⓑ   100

    Ⓒ   200

    Ⓓ   300

6   Estimate how many more cans were collected by the third-grade class than the second-grade class.

    Ⓕ   About 50

    Ⓖ   About 150

    Ⓗ   About 250

    Ⓙ   About 650

SOL 3.1 The student will read and write six-digit numerals and identify the place value for each digit.
SOL 3.8 The student will solve problems ... using various computational methods, including ...mental computation, and estimation.
SOL 3.24 The student will ... describe ... patterns ... and extend the pattern....

Lesson 2-12   Name _____

Use the table for 1-3.

School Clothes	Price
Sweater	$29
T-Shirt	$ 8
Jeans	$17
Shoes	$45

1 The table gives the prices of some school clothes. Matt has $50. Which items of clothing can he buy?

   Ⓐ   A sweater and a pair of shoes

   Ⓑ   2 sweaters

   Ⓒ   3 pairs of jeans

   Ⓓ   A sweater and a pair of jeans

2 Which items of clothing could you buy with 4 ten-dollar bills?

   Ⓕ   A pair of shoes

   Ⓖ   2 sweaters

   Ⓗ   A sweater and a T-shirt

   Ⓙ   A pair of jeans and a sweater

3 Jackson has 4 one-dollar bills, 2 five-dollar bills and 3 ten-dollar bills. How much money does he have?

   Ⓐ $9

   Ⓑ $16

   Ⓒ $39

   Ⓓ $44

4 Which number is shown by the place value blocks?

   Ⓕ   11

   Ⓖ   38

   Ⓗ   308

   Ⓙ   380

5 Andrew said, "163 is the same as —

   Ⓐ   16 tens

   Ⓑ   16 tens and 63 ones

   Ⓒ   1 hundred and 63 tens

   Ⓓ   16 tens and 3 ones

6 There are 324 cupcakes at the 9 A.M. start of the bake sale at Maymont Elementary School in Richmond. Each hour 5 dozen or 60 cupcakes were sold. How many cupcakes were left at 10 A.M., 11 A.M., noon? What is the pattern?

Answer: _____

_____

_____

27

Lesson 2-13   Name _____

1 Mr. Jackson flew 49 miles from Lynchburg to Waynesboro. Then he flew 22 miles to Charlottesville. Use mental math to find how many miles he flew in all.

Ⓐ 60

Ⓑ 61

Ⓒ 70

Ⓓ 71

2 Maggie's class collected 393 labels last week and 405 labels this week. They need 1,000 labels in all. What is the best estimate for the number of labels they have collected?

Ⓕ 700

Ⓖ 800

Ⓗ 900

Ⓙ 1,000

3 Steve solved 83 − 17 by adding the same number to each. Which number did he add?

Ⓐ 4

Ⓑ 3

Ⓒ 2

Ⓓ 1

4 Kevin estimated each sum by rounding. Which is an underestimate?

Ⓕ 19 + 27 is about 50

Ⓖ 78 + 55 is about 140

Ⓗ 34 + 253 is about 280

Ⓙ 347 + 196 is about 550

5 Which two numbers have a sum of about 230?

Ⓐ 56 and 82

Ⓑ 131 and 97

Ⓒ 142 and 49

Ⓓ 178 and 72

6 Which of the following number sentences can be used to find how many more nickels there are than quarters?

Ⓕ 13 + 4 = ☐

Ⓖ 13 − 4 = ☐

Ⓗ 13 − 9 = ☐

Ⓙ 13 + ☐ = 4

7 Which of the following shows a way to break apart numbers in order to find 58 + 47 mentally?

Ⓐ 5 + 4 and 8 + 7

Ⓑ 50 + 50 and 8 − 7

Ⓒ 50 + 40 and 8 + 7

Ⓓ 50 + 50 and 90 − 7

Lesson 3-1   Name _____

1 Find the sum of 66 and 28.

    (A) 38

    (B) 48

    (C) 84

    (D) 94

2 There are 26 children in the choir and 37 children in the school band. How many children are in the choir and band?

    (F) 53

    (G) 63

    (H) 73

    (J) 83

3 Which two numbers will have the greatest sum?

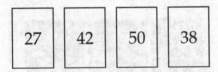

| 27 | 42 | 50 | 38 |

    (A) 38 and 42

    (B) 27 and 50

    (C) 50 and 42

    (D) 38 and 27

4 Estimate to find the number sentence that is correct.

    (F) $23 + 67 = 80$

    (G) $34 + 76 = 100$

    (H) $48 + 82 = 130$

    (J) $46 + 37 = 713$

5 There are 2 bags of soybeans. One bag weighs 47 pounds. The other bag weighs 39 pounds. How many pounds of soybeans are there in the bags?

    (A) 76 pounds

    (B) 78 pounds

    (C) 86 pounds

    (D) 88 pounds

6 Find the sum.

$$83 + 47$$

    (F) 110

    (G) 120

    (H) 130

    (J) 140

7 In Charlottesville, the average yearly rainfall is between 44 and 48 inches. *About* how much rainfall does Charlottesville get in 2 years?

    (A) About 44 inches

    (B) About 48 inches

    (C) About 92 inches

    (D) About 100 inches

8 What is the missing number?

$$\begin{array}{r} 3\square \\ + \underline{49} \\ 86 \end{array}$$

    (F) 3

    (G) 7

    (H) 33

    (J) 37

Lesson 3-2   Name _____

1 Jason used place-value blocks to solve a problem. How did he write the problem and sum for these place-value blocks?

ⓐ 356 + 124 = 480

ⓑ 356 − 142 = 214

ⓒ 356 + 142 = 498

ⓓ 365 + 124 = 489

2 Find the sum.

$$318 + 172$$

Ⓕ 480

Ⓖ 490

Ⓗ 500

Ⓙ 318,172

3 Which of the following does *not* show the sum of 359 + 174 using place-value blocks?

ⓐ 4 hundreds, 12 tens, 13 ones

ⓑ 4 hundreds, 3 tens, 3 ones

ⓒ 4 hundreds, 13 tens, 3 ones

ⓓ 5 hundreds, 3 tens, 3 ones

4 There are 157 students in the third grade and 163 students in the fourth grade. Which place-value model shows how many students there are?

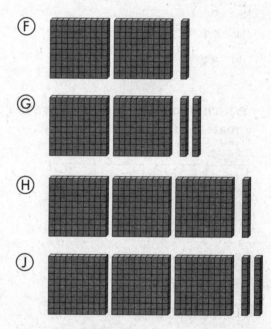

5 Ken used place-value blocks to solve a problem. When he combined the blocks, he had 4 hundreds, 14 tens, and 7 ones. What are two possible addends in the problem he solved?

_____

Explain how you found your answer.

_____

_____

Lesson 3-3   Name _____

1
$$\begin{array}{r} 364 \\ + \ 246 \end{array}$$

Ⓐ 500

Ⓑ 510

Ⓒ 600

Ⓓ 610

2   612 + 295 =

Ⓕ 807

Ⓖ 817

Ⓗ 907

Ⓙ 917

3   To find the answer to this problem,

$$\begin{array}{r} 374 \\ + \ 241 \end{array}$$

Ryan —

Ⓐ did not have to regroup

Ⓑ regrouped once

Ⓒ regrouped twice

Ⓓ regrouped three times

4   What is the sum?

Ⓕ 292

Ⓖ 302

Ⓗ 312

Ⓙ 392

Use the table for 5–6.

Cities in Virginia	Miles Apart
Bristol to Roanoke	131
Bristol to Norfolk	329
Roanoke to Alexandria	189
Norfolk to Roanoke	206

5   The table gives the distances in miles between some cities in Virginia. Kim traveled from Bristol to Roanoke and then from Roanoke to Norfolk. How many miles did she travel?

Ⓐ 131

Ⓑ 206

Ⓒ 337

Ⓓ 347

6   Ethan traveled from Bristol to Roanoke and then from Roanoke to Alexandria. How many miles did he travel?

Ⓕ 131

Ⓖ 189

Ⓗ 310

Ⓙ 320

7   Estimate to decide which sum is greater than 1,000.

Ⓐ 498 + 399

Ⓑ 538 + 419

Ⓒ 706 + 235

Ⓓ 461 + 575

Lesson 3-4   Name _____

1   **Find the sum.**

$$38$$
$$19$$
$$+\ 56$$

(A)   93

(B)   97

(C)   103

(D)   113

2   **Find the sum.**

$$164$$
$$275$$
$$+\ 622$$

(F)   951

(G)   961

(H)   1,061

(J)   1,151

3   **Use mental math to find the sum.**

$$275 + 63 + 25$$

(A)   283

(B)   363

(C)   About 380

(D)   About 400

4   **Find the sum.**

$$187 + 36 + 209$$

(F)   322

(G)   422

(H)   432

(J)   646

Use the table for 5–7.

Name	Number of Cans Collected
Grade 2	245
Grade 3	409
Grade 4	172
Grade 5	317

5   The table shows the number of tin cans that were collected in one week for the Great Clean Up Week in Pulaski. How many cans did grades 2, 3, and 5 collect?

(A)   611

(B)   951

(C)   971

(D)   1,051

6   How many cans did all 4 classes collect?

(F)   172

(G)   1,043

(H)   1,133

(J)   1,143

7   Grade 6 collected 399 cans. How many cans did Grades 3, 5 and 6 collect?

(A)   716

(B)   808

(C)   1,053

(D)   1,125

Lesson 3-5   Name _____

1 Matt and Caleb are washing dishes.
Matt washes 3 dishes in the time it
takes Caleb to wash 2 dishes. If Matt
washes 12 dishes, how many dishes
will Caleb wash in the same amount
of time?

Ⓐ 4
Ⓑ 6
Ⓒ 8
Ⓓ 9

2 During the hot dog eating contest at
the fair, Josh eats 5 hot dogs in the
time it takes Seth to eat 3 hot dogs.
When Josh has eaten 15 hot dogs,
how many has Seth eaten?

Ⓕ 6
Ⓖ 7
Ⓗ 8
Ⓙ 9

3 Emma is making a bracelet. She puts
5 yellow beads on the chain, then
2 blue beads, then 5 yellow beads,
then 2 blue beads, and continues the
pattern. After she uses 8 blue beads,
how many yellow beads has she
used?

Ⓐ 25
Ⓑ 20
Ⓒ 15
Ⓓ 10

4 Alice rides her bike 2 miles on
Monday and 4 miles on Tuesday. She
rides 2 miles on Wednesday and 4
miles on Thursday. If this pattern
continues, how many days will it
take Alice to ride 30 miles in total?

Ⓕ 6
Ⓖ 8
Ⓗ 10
Ⓙ 12

5 Adam is choosing what he wants for breakfast in Williamsburg.
He can choose from pancakes, cereal or eggs. For his drink, he
can choose from orange juice or milk. How many different
combinations of breakfast are possible?

Draw a picture to solve the problem.

Answer: _____ breakfasts

33

Lesson 3-6   Name _____

1 **Regroup 1 ten as 10 ones in 78.**

Ⓐ 17 tens and 8 ones

Ⓑ 7 tens and 8 ones

Ⓒ 6 tens and 8 ones

Ⓓ 6 tens and 18 ones

2 **Regroup 1 ten as 10 ones in 90.**

Ⓕ 8 tens and 0 ones

Ⓖ 8 tens and 10 ones

Ⓗ 9 tens and 0 ones

Ⓙ 19 tens and 0 ones

3 **In the number 309, how many tens is the same as 3 hundreds?**

Ⓐ 13

Ⓑ 30

Ⓒ 39

Ⓓ 300

4 **Which numbers go in the boxes for this regrouping?**

$$407 = \textbf{4} \; \textbf{0} \; \textbf{7}$$

Ⓕ 3 and 0

Ⓖ 3 and 10

Ⓗ 4 and 1

Ⓙ 4 and 10

5   **450 =**

Ⓐ 4 hundreds, 5 ones

Ⓑ 4 hundreds, 50 tens

Ⓒ 3 hundreds, 15 tens

Ⓓ 3 hundreds, 50 ones

6 **Regroup 1 hundred as 10 tens in 365.**

Ⓕ 2 hundreds, 6 tens, 15 ones

Ⓖ 2 hundreds, 16 tens, 5 ones

Ⓗ 3 hundreds, 5 tens, 15 ones

Ⓙ 3 hundreds, 6 tens, 5 ones

7 **However you regroup 345, you will always have at *least* —**

Ⓐ 4 hundreds

Ⓑ 40 tens

Ⓒ 45 ones

Ⓓ 5 ones

8 **After regrouping 1 hundred as 10 tens, Andrew has 2 hundreds, 14 tens, and 6 ones. Which number did he regroup?**

Ⓕ 246

Ⓖ 346

Ⓗ 364

Ⓙ 446

Lesson 3-7   Name _____

1 Find the difference.

$$\begin{array}{r} 94 \\ -\ 49 \\ \hline \end{array}$$

(A) 40

(B) 45

(C) 50

(D) 55

2 Find the difference when 36 is subtracted from 85.

(F) 41

(G) 49

(H) 51

(J) 59

3 Find the difference.

$$70 - 23 =$$

(A) 47

(B) 53

(C) 57

(D) 93

4 Casey has read 58 pages in a book with 92 pages. How many more pages does she still have to read?

(F) 34

(G) 44

(H) 140

(J) 150

5 Which of these problems needs regrouping to solve?

(A) 50 – 20

(B) 58 – 20

(C) 58 – 28

(D) 50 – 28

6 The distance from Richmond to Chesapeake is 87 miles. Mr. Adams drove 38 miles. How many miles does he have left to drive until he gets to Chesapeake?

(F) 59

(G) 51

(H) 49

(J) 125

7 The final score in a basketball game was 93 to 58. How many more points did the winning team score?

(A) 25

(B) 35

(C) 45

(D) 55

8 What is the missing number?

$$\begin{array}{r} 83 \\ -\ \square 9 \\ \hline 24 \end{array}$$

(F) 5

(G) 6

(H) 40

(J) 60

35

Lesson 3-8   Name _____

1 Kevin used place-value blocks to solve a problem. How did he write the problem and difference for these place-value blocks?

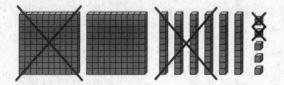

   Ⓐ 265 + 124 = 389

   Ⓑ 265 − 142 = 123

   Ⓒ 265 − 124 = 141

   Ⓓ 256 − 142 = 114

2 Find the difference.

      458 − 383

   Ⓕ 75

   Ⓖ 95

   Ⓗ 125

   Ⓙ 135

3 Noah has 164 baseball cards. Randy has 138 baseball cards. Which place-value model shows how many more baseball cards Noah has?

   Ⓐ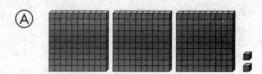

   Ⓑ

   Ⓒ

   Ⓓ

4 Which of the following shows the difference of 263 − 98 using place-value blocks?

   Ⓕ 1 hundred, 7 tens, 5 ones

   Ⓖ 1 hundred, 6 tens, 5 ones

   Ⓗ 2 hundreds, 6 tens, 5 ones

   Ⓙ 2 hundreds, 3 tens, 3 ones

5 Gary counted 193 Virginia license plates during his trip along Highway 81. Reba counted 87 Virginia license plates. How many more Virginia license plates did Gary count than Reba? Write the problem and difference.

Answer: _____

Explain or draw pictures to show how you regrouped to subtract 7 ones.

_____

_____

Lesson 3-9   Name _____

1   435
          − 193

   Ⓐ 142

   Ⓑ 242

   Ⓒ 362

   Ⓓ 628

2   336 − 128 =

   Ⓕ 152

   Ⓖ 208

   Ⓗ 212

   Ⓙ 464

3   354 − 124 = 230

      354 − 125 =

   Ⓐ 231

   Ⓑ 229

   Ⓒ 221

   Ⓓ 199

4 Using this model, what is the difference when you subtract 74?

   Ⓕ 104

   Ⓖ 196

   Ⓗ 204

   Ⓙ 352

5 Maria subtracted 319 from 521 and got 118. Maria's answer —

   Ⓐ is reasonable because
      500 − 400 = 100

   Ⓑ is reasonable because
      520 − 300 = 180

   Ⓒ is unreasonable because
      600 − 400 = 200

   Ⓓ is unreasonable because
      500 − 300 = 200

6 The distance from Bristol to Charlottesville is 225 miles. Juan has traveled 78 miles from Bristol towards Charlottesville. How many more miles does he have to travel to reach Charlottesville?

   Ⓕ 303 miles

   Ⓖ 253 miles

   Ⓗ 157 miles

   Ⓙ 147 miles

7 To find the answer to this problem,

      345
     − 249

Ryan —

   Ⓐ did not have to regroup

   Ⓑ regrouped once

   Ⓒ regrouped twice

   Ⓓ regrouped three times

Lesson 3-10   Name _____

1
$$\begin{array}{r} 503 \\ -\ 345 \\ \hline \end{array}$$

- Ⓐ 848
- Ⓑ 242
- Ⓒ 168
- Ⓓ 158

2 Hal has 120 toy cars. He donated 65 of them to a children's hospital. How many cars does he have left?

- Ⓕ 45
- Ⓖ 55
- Ⓗ 65
- Ⓙ 75

3 Find the difference.

$$400 - 177 =$$

- Ⓐ 223
- Ⓑ 323
- Ⓒ 377
- Ⓓ 577

4 Raymond is loading boxes on a truck. There are 370 boxes. Raymond has loaded 297 boxes. Which number sentence shows how many more boxes Raymond has to load?

- Ⓕ 370 − 297 = 127
- Ⓖ 370 + 297 = 667
- Ⓗ 370 − 297 = 83
- Ⓙ 370 − 297 = 73

5 To find 204 − 126, you can regroup 204 to —

- Ⓐ 19 tens and 4 ones
- Ⓑ 19 tens and 14 ones
- Ⓒ 18 tens and 14 ones
- Ⓓ 18 tens and 34 ones

6 The drawing shows that the greatest north-south distance in Virginia is 201 miles. The greatest north-south distance in Tennessee is 116 miles. How much greater is the north-south distance in Virginia?

- Ⓕ 85 miles
- Ⓖ 95 miles
- Ⓗ 105 miles
- Ⓙ 115 miles

7 Tom subtracted 179 from 500 and got 421. How can he use estimation to check his answer and find out he was wrong?

- Ⓐ 500 − 100 = 400
- Ⓑ 500 − 200 = 300
- Ⓒ 500 + 180 = 680
- Ⓓ 500 + 200 = 700

Lesson 3-11   Name _____

1 Miss Diego wants to bake enough muffins for her class of 28 students. Her recipe makes 12 in a batch. How many batches must she bake to have enough cookies for the class?

(A) 2 batches

(B) 3 batches

(C) 4 batches

(D) 5 batches

2 Mateo collects coins. He has 24 state quarters, 23 buffalo nickels, and 14 Mercury dimes. About how many coins does he have?

(F) 40

(G) 50

(H) 60

(J) 70

3 Leon is filling gift bags for his brother's birthday party. He must fill bags for 14 girls and 12 boys. How many bags must he fill?

(A) About 40

(B) About 50

(C) Exactly 26

(D) Exactly 28

Use the table for 4–5.

Betsy's Bakery	Servings (per item)
Large pecan pie	8
Regular apple pie	6
Small sheet cake	24
Box of cookies	15

4 The table shows how many servings are in each type of baked item at Betsy's Bakery. What's the greatest number of people that can be served if someone buys 4 large pecan pies?

(F) 8

(G) 12

(H) 24

(J) 32

5 Kevin needs to buy enough sheet cakes for everyone in the third grade to have at least one serving of cake at the school picnic. How many sheet cakes should he buy if there are 88 students in the third grade?

(A) 2

(B) 3

(C) 4

(D) 10

Lesson 3-12

Name _____

1
$$\begin{array}{r} \$5.09 \\ +\ \$3.98 \end{array}$$

Ⓐ $1.11

Ⓑ $2.11

Ⓒ $8.97

Ⓓ $9.07

2
$$\begin{array}{r} \$10.00 \\ -\ \$6.43 \end{array}$$

Ⓕ $3.57

Ⓖ $3.67

Ⓗ $4.57

Ⓙ $4.67

3 Jessica wants to buy a sweater for $14.98. If she pays with a $20 bill, how much change should she get back?

Ⓐ $4.02

Ⓑ $5.02

Ⓒ $6.02

Ⓓ $6.98

Use the table for 4–5.

Food Item	Price
Turkey roll-up	$1.75
Hamburger	$2.29
Ham sandwich	$3.55
Tuna salad	$2.98

4 The table gives the prices of food items in a Danville restaurant. How much does a turkey roll-up and tuna salad cost?

Ⓕ $4.04

Ⓖ $5.30

Ⓗ $4.73

Ⓙ $5.75

5 Marty bought a ham sandwich. How much change should he get back if he pays with a $5 bill?

Ⓐ $3.55

Ⓑ $3.45

Ⓒ $2.45

Ⓓ $1.45

6 Katy bought three items at the grocery store in Portsmouth. The total came to $12.65. Katy gave the clerk a $20 bill. The clerk gave Kay a $5 bill, a quarter, and a dime. Was this the correct change?

Explain your answer using words, tables, diagrams or pictures.

_____

_____

Lesson 3-13   Name _____

1 Cody wants to find the exact answer to this problem. Which method would be easiest to use?

$$
\begin{array}{r}
13,115 \\
4,959 \\
+\ 27,146 \\
\hline
\end{array}
$$

Ⓐ Estimation

Ⓑ Mental math

Ⓒ Pencil and Paper

Ⓓ Calculator

2 Aretha found the exact answer to this problem very quickly. Which method do you think she used?

$$
\begin{array}{r}
530 \\
-\ 400 \\
\hline
\end{array}
$$

Ⓕ Estimation

Ⓖ Mental math

Ⓗ Pencil and paper

Ⓙ Calculator

3 Kareem found the exact answer to this problem and then he added to check his answer without using a calculator. Which method do you think he used to find the difference?

$$
\begin{array}{r}
539 \\
-\ 274 \\
\hline
\end{array}
$$

Ⓐ Estimation

Ⓑ Mental math

Ⓒ Pencil and paper

Ⓓ Calculator

4 Which method do you think Carlos used to check if the sum was more than 800?

$$
\begin{array}{r}
293 \\
+\ 566 \\
\hline
\end{array}
$$

Ⓕ Estimation

Ⓖ Mental math

Ⓗ Pencil and paper

Ⓙ Calculator

5 To find 76 − 43, would you use paper and pencil, mental math, estimation, or a calculator? Explain your choice. Then find the answer.

_____

_____

Answer: _____

Lesson 3-14   Name _____

1 Which statement is true?

- Ⓐ 14 + 7 < 34 − 11
- Ⓑ 14 + 7 = 34 − 11
- Ⓒ 14 + 7 > 34 − 11
- Ⓓ 14 − 7 > 34 − 11

2 Which number makes this statement true?

$$16 + 108 + \rule{2cm}{0.4pt} > 200$$

- Ⓕ 55
- Ⓖ 65
- Ⓗ 75
- Ⓙ 85

3 Which symbol goes in the box to make this number sentence true?

$$49 + 38 \ \square\ 162 - 75$$

- Ⓐ >
- Ⓑ =
- Ⓒ <
- Ⓓ +

4 Which number makes this statement true?

$$25 + x > 50$$

- Ⓕ 15
- Ⓖ 20
- Ⓗ 25
- Ⓙ 30

5 Which 3 numbers all make this statement true?

$$16 + \square < 20$$

- Ⓐ 1, 2, 3
- Ⓑ 4, 5, 6
- Ⓒ 2, 3, 4
- Ⓓ 3, 4, 5

6 Roger arranged the following number cards and symbol cards to make a true number sentence. Which number sentence did he make?

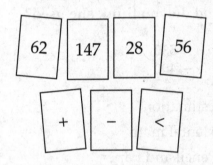

- Ⓕ 56 + 62 = 147 − 28
- Ⓖ 147 − 62 < 56 + 28
- Ⓗ 62 + 28 < 147 − 56
- Ⓙ 147 − 28 < 56 + 62

SOL 3.2 The student will round a whole number, 9,999 or less, to the nearest ... hundred....
SOL 3.8 The student will solve problems involving the sum or difference of two whole numbers, each 9,999 or less, with or without regrouping, using various computational methods, including ... paper and pencil....

Lesson 3-15   Name _____

Use the table for 1–3.

Cities in Virginia	Miles Apart
Bristol to Roanoke	131
Bristol to Norfolk	329
Roanoke to Alexandria	189
Norfolk to Roanoke	206

1 The table gives the distances in miles between some cities in Virginia. Round the distance from Bristol to Norfolk to the nearest hundred.

Ⓐ 100

Ⓑ 200

Ⓒ 300

Ⓓ 400

2 How much farther is it from Bristol to Norfolk than from Bristol to Roanoke?

Ⓕ 188 miles

Ⓖ 198 miles

Ⓗ 218 miles

Ⓙ 450 miles

3 David traveled from Norfolk to Bristol followed by Roanoke. How many miles did he travel?

Ⓐ 198

Ⓑ 218

Ⓒ 337

Ⓓ 460

4 Sam had 203 pennies. He gave 78 pennies to his sister. How many pennies does Sam have left?

Ⓕ 125

Ⓖ 135

Ⓗ 165

Ⓙ 175

5 Sarah collects foreign stamps. She has 28 from Canada, 37 from Mexico, and 16 from England. How many stamps does she have in her collection?

Ⓐ 61

Ⓑ 71

Ⓒ 81

Ⓓ 91

6 Find the difference.

$$600 - 253 = \boxed{}$$

Ⓕ 453

Ⓖ 447

Ⓗ 357

Ⓙ 347

7 Estimate the sum for 493 + 275.

Ⓐ 600

Ⓑ 700

Ⓒ 800

Ⓓ 900

Lesson 4-1   Name _____

1   The clock shows the time the last tour of Jefferson's home at Monticello started. What time did the last tour start?

(A) 9:05 P.M.   (C) 5:45 P.M.

(B) 6:45 P.M.   (D) 4:45 P.M.

2   When Marisa got up this morning, her clock showed the following time. What time did Marisa get up?

(F) Fifteen minutes to seven

(G) Quarter to seven

(H) Quarter past seven

(J) Seven o'clock

3   Which of the following clocks shows nine thirty?

(A)   (C)

(B)   (D)

4   Denise said that the time was 12:15. Which of the following clocks shows the time 12:15?

(F)

(G)

(H)

(J)

5   The movie ends at the time shown on the clock below.

Which does NOT show the time on the clock?

(A) Eight forty-five

(B) 15 minutes after 9

(C) Quarter to nine

(D) 15 minutes to nine

Lesson 4-2   Name _____

1 The clock shows the time the airplane landed at the Richmond airport.

What time did the plane land?

Ⓐ 11:28

Ⓑ 11:43

Ⓒ 11:48

Ⓓ 11:53

2 Mel's soccer game started at the time shown on the clock below.

Which does NOT show the time on the clock?

Ⓕ Nine fifty

Ⓖ 10 minutes to 9

Ⓗ 50 minutes past 9

Ⓙ 10 minutes to 10

3 The clock below shows the time Inez started her walk around the park. What time did Inez start walking?

Ⓐ 1:13

Ⓑ 2:07

Ⓒ 3:07

Ⓓ 4:03

4 The sun rose over Shenandoah National Park at 5:38 A.M. Which of the following clocks shows that time?

Ⓕ    Ⓗ

Ⓖ    Ⓙ

5 Which is the time on the clock?

Ⓐ 5 minutes past 7

Ⓑ 5 minutes after 8

Ⓒ 50 minutes after 7

Ⓓ 5 minutes to 8

Lesson 4-3   Name _____

1 A birthday party at the Charlottesville Children's Museum started at 1:30. The clock shows the time the party ended. How long was the party?

Ⓐ 30 minutes

Ⓑ 1 hour 30 minutes

Ⓒ 2 hours

Ⓓ 2 hours 30 minutes

2 Jason got up at 7:05 A.M. He left for school 45 minutes later. What time did Jason leave for school?

Ⓕ 7:40 A.M.   Ⓗ 7:50 A.M.

Ⓖ 7:45 A.M.   Ⓙ 7:55 A.M.

3 Blaire read a biography about James Monroe, a U.S. President from Virginia. She started reading at 12:30 P.M. and finished at 3:00 P.M. For how long did Blaire read?

Ⓐ 30 minutes

Ⓑ 2 hours 30 minutes

Ⓒ 3 hours

Ⓓ 3 hours 30 minutes

4 Mr. Larsen left Richmond at 10:45 A.M. He arrived in Roanoke at 2:00 P.M. How long was the trip?

Ⓕ 3 hours 15 minutes

Ⓖ 3 hours 45 minutes

Ⓗ 4 hours 15 minutes

Ⓙ 4 hours 45 minutes

5 The music recital started at 5:00 P.M. It ended at this time:

How long did the recital last?

Ⓐ 1 hour 45 minutes

Ⓑ 1 hour 15 minutes

Ⓒ 1 hour 5 minutes

Ⓓ 45 minutes

6 When the bus arrived at 4:00 P.M., Scott had been at the bus stop for 20 minutes. When did he arrive?

Ⓕ 4:20 P.M.   Ⓗ 3:30 P.M.

Ⓖ 3:40 P.M.   Ⓙ 3:20 P.M.

7 Corey went to Colonial Williamsburg. She arrived at 1:30 P.M. and stayed for 3 hours and 40 minutes. What time did she leave? Explain your answer using words or pictures.

Lesson 4-4   Name _____

1 **What day of the week is July 23?**

July						
S	M	T	W	T	F	S
		1	2	3	4	5
6	7	8	9	10	11	12
13	14	15	16	17	18	19
20	21	22	23	24	25	26
27	28	29	30	31		

Ⓐ Sunday

Ⓑ Monday

Ⓒ Tuesday

Ⓓ Wednesday

2 **Virginia became a state on June 25, 1788. In 2004, June 27 is on Sunday. On what day of the week does Virginia celebrate statehood in 2004?**

Ⓕ Tuesday   Ⓗ Thursday

Ⓖ Wednesday   Ⓙ Friday

3 **Travis has soccer practice every Thursday. How many times does he have soccer practice in May?**

May 2004						
S	M	T	W	T	F	S
						1
2	3	4	5	6	7	8
9	10	11	12	13	14	15
16	17	18	19	20	21	22
23	24	25	26	27	28	29
30	31					

Ⓐ 3

Ⓑ 4

Ⓒ 5

Ⓓ 7

4 **Jenny has a dentist appointment exactly one week from March 16. What date is the dentist appointment?**

March						
S	M	T	W	T	F	S
	1	2	3	4	5	6
7	8	9	10	11	12	13
14	15	16	17	18	19	20
21	22	23	24	25	26	27
28	29	30				

Ⓕ March 2

Ⓖ March 9

Ⓗ March 23

Ⓙ March 30

5 **Steven's birthday is in 2 weeks. How many days until Steve's birthday?**

Ⓐ 2 days

Ⓑ 7 days

Ⓒ 14 days

Ⓓ 21 days

6 **What is the tenth month of the year?**

Ⓕ September

Ⓖ October

Ⓗ November

Ⓙ December

7 **Debra started her art project on Friday, April 2. She finished the project on the next Monday. On which date did she finish?**

Ⓐ April 3   Ⓒ April 5

Ⓑ April 4   Ⓓ April 6

Lesson 4-5   Name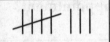

1 How many students chose ice cream as their favorite dessert?

Ice Cream	☰☰☰☰☰ |||

Ⓐ 5
Ⓑ 7
Ⓒ 8
Ⓓ 13

2 How would you show the number 13 on a tally chart?

Ⓕ 卌 ||

Ⓖ 卌 卌 |||

Ⓗ 卌 ||||

Ⓙ 卌 |||

3 Use the data in the tally chart. Which flavor did 11 people choose?

Favorite Yogurt Flavor

Vanilla	卌 卌	
Strawberry	卌 卌 |||
Blueberry	卌 ||
Raspberry	卌	

Ⓐ Vanilla
Ⓑ Strawberry
Ⓒ Blueberry
Ⓓ Raspberry

4 Which shows 21 tally marks?

Ⓕ 卌 卌 卌 卌 卌

Ⓖ 卌 卌 卌 卌 |

Ⓗ 卌 卌 卌 |

Ⓙ 卌 卌 |

5 The tally chart shows the favorite pets of children in a Danville Elementary School. How many children voted for cats and dogs?

Favorite Pet

Dog	卌 ||
Cat	卌
Bird	||||

Ⓐ 7
Ⓑ 12
Ⓒ 15
Ⓓ 16

6 Use the data in the tally chart. How many more children take a bus to school than walk to school?

How We Get to School

Walk	卌	
Car	卌 卌 ||
Bus	卌 卌 卌

Ⓕ 21   Ⓗ 9
Ⓖ 10   Ⓙ 6

Lesson 4-6   Name _____

1   The line plot shows the ages of students who participated in a karate tournament in Lynchburg. How many were 8 years old?

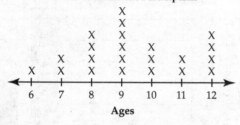

Karate Tournament Participants

Ages

Ⓐ 3   Ⓒ 5

Ⓑ 4   Ⓓ 6

2   The line plot shows how tourists scored on a game at a Virginia Beach arcade. How many scored 95 or higher?

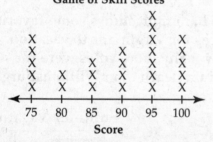

Game of Skill Scores

Score

Ⓕ 3   Ⓗ 12

Ⓖ 7   Ⓙ 14

3   The line plot shows how far some children live from the library. How many children live 7 miles or less from the library?

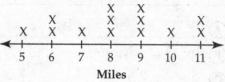

Distance From Library

Miles

Ⓐ 1   Ⓒ 4

Ⓑ 3   Ⓓ 7

4   The line plot shows the number of pets owned by students. How many pets do the students own in all?

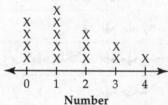

Pets Owned

Number

Ⓕ 21   Ⓗ 10

Ⓖ 11   Ⓙ 4

5   Look at the line plot for Pets Owned in 4. What is the mode of the data. Explain how you know.

_____

_____

Lesson 4-7   Name _____

1 The picture graph shows how much snow fell in two months.

Inches of Snowfall

December	❄ ❄
January	❄ ❄ ❄ ❄

Each ❄ = 3 inches

How much snow fell in January?

Ⓐ 3 inches   Ⓒ 6 inches

Ⓑ 4 inches   Ⓓ 12 inches

2 Sonya's scout troop made a picture graph to show their favorite birds.

Favorite Birds

Robin	↓ ↓ ↓
Nuthatch	↓ ↓ ↓ ↓ ↓
Crow	↓ ↓
Cardinal	↓ ↓ ↓ ↓ ↓ ↓ ↓

Each ↓ = 2 scouts

How many more scouts chose the cardinal than the robin?

Ⓕ 4   Ⓗ 8

Ⓖ 6   Ⓙ 10

3 On a picture graph, each symbol stands for 5 apples. How many apples do 3 symbols represent on the graph?

Ⓐ 35   Ⓒ 10

Ⓑ 15   Ⓓ 3

4 The bar graph shows some children's costumes. Which is the favorite costume of the most children?

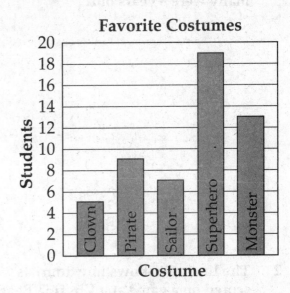

Ⓕ Superhero   Ⓗ Monster

Ⓖ Pirate   Ⓙ Clown

5 The bar graph shows some favorite places for Virginians to vacation. How many more votes were for Viginia Beach than Williamsburg?

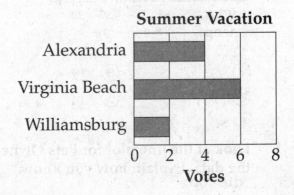

Ⓐ 2   Ⓒ 4

Ⓑ 3   Ⓓ 6

50

SOL 3.8 The student will solve problems involving the sum or difference ... using various computational methods, including ... paper and pencil.... SOL 3.22 The student will read and interpret data represented in ... bar ... and picture graphs.... SOL 3.24 The student will recognize and describe a variety of patterns ... and extend the pattern, using the same or different forms (... numbers ...).

Lesson 4-8   Name _____

The bar graph shows how many volunteers will work at a Manassas car wash each hour. Use the bar graph for 1–2.

The picture graph below shows how much snow fell in each of 4 months. Use the picture graph for 3–5.

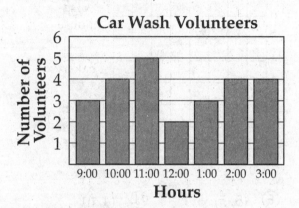

Number of Inches of Snow

December	❄❄❄❄
January	❄❄❄
February	❄❄
March	❄

Each ❄ = 3 inches of snow

1   Use the bar graph to find which statement is true.

Ⓐ The most volunteers will be there at 1:00.

Ⓑ There will be 4 volunteers at 9:00.

Ⓒ There will be 3 volunteers at 12:00.

Ⓓ There will be the same number of volunteers at 10:00 and 2:00.

3   Use the graph to find which statement is true.

Ⓐ More snow fell in January than in December.

Ⓑ The amount of snow decreased each month from December on.

Ⓒ The amount of snow did not change from December to March.

Ⓓ More snow fell in March than in December.

2   At which time will the least number of people volunteer at the car wash?

Ⓕ 9:00   Ⓗ 11:00

Ⓖ 10:00   Ⓙ 12:00

4   How many inches of snow fell in the months of February and March?

Ⓕ 3   Ⓗ 9

Ⓖ 6   Ⓙ 12

5   Write your own statement that compares the data on the picture graph.

_____

_____

Lesson 4-9   Name _____

1 The coordinates of the pet store are —

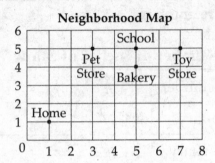

Neighborhood Map

Ⓐ (5, 4)   Ⓒ (5, 5)

Ⓑ (7, 5)   Ⓓ (3, 5)

2 Which ordered pair describes the location of S?

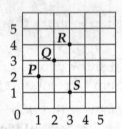

Ⓕ (1, 2)   Ⓗ (3, 4)

Ⓖ (2, 3)   Ⓙ (3, 1)

3 The map below shows some animals at the zoo. Which animals are found at (5, 3)?

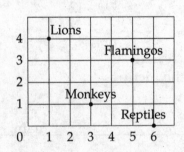

Ⓐ Flamingos   Ⓒ Lions

Ⓑ Monkeys   Ⓓ Reptiles

4 The lake is located at —

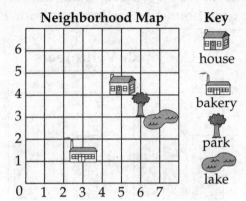

Neighborhood Map   Key

Ⓕ (5, 5)   Ⓗ (4, 6)

Ⓖ (7, 3)   Ⓙ (6, 3)

5 The point named by (2, 3) is —

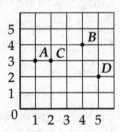

Ⓐ A   Ⓒ C

Ⓑ B   Ⓓ D

6 Which neighborhood place is found at (1, 5)?

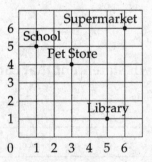

Ⓕ School   Ⓗ Supermarket

Ⓖ Pet Store   Ⓙ Library

Lesson 4-10   Name _____

1   The line graph shows the number of meets the swim team won.

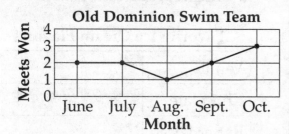

How many meets did the swim team win in October?

(A) 1   (C) 3

(B) 2   (D) 4

Use the line graph for 2 and 3.

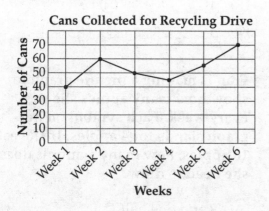

2   How long did the recycling drive last?

(F) 1 week   (H) 7 weeks

(G) 6 weeks   (J) 70 weeks

3   During which week were the most cans collected?

(A) Week 2   (C) Week 5

(B) Week 3   (D) Week 6

4   The line graph shows the number of hours Clay worked each week for 5 weeks.

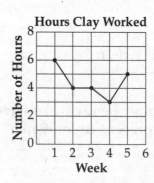

During which two weeks did Clay work the same number of hours?

(F) Week 1 and Week 2

(G) Week 2 and Week 3

(H) Week 3 and Week 4

(J) Week 4 and Week 5

5   The line graph shows how many points a third grade basketball team scored in each of 5 games.

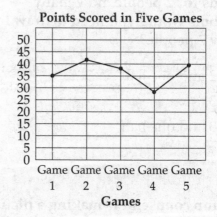

During which game did the team score 35 points?

(A) Game 1   (C) Game 3

(B) Game 2   (D) Game 4

Lesson 4-11   Name _____

1 Jenny is making a picture graph using the key shown below.

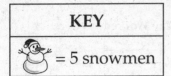

KEY
= 5 snowmen

How many snowmen will she have to draw to represent 10 snowmen?

Ⓐ 1

Ⓑ 2

Ⓒ 5

Ⓓ 10

2 Where should Selena look on a picture graph to find out what each symbol stands for?

Ⓕ Title   Ⓗ Scale

Ⓖ Symbol   Ⓙ Key

3 If each symbol on a picture graph stands for 2 people, how many symbols would you need to draw to show 7 people?

Ⓐ 2 and one half

Ⓑ 3

Ⓒ 3 and one half

Ⓓ 7

4 Rodrigo's class is finishing the picture graph below to show their favorite ice cream flavors.

Favorite Ice Cream Flavors

Vanilla	
Chocolate	🍦🍦🍦🍦🍦🍦
Butter Pecan	🍦🍦
Strawberry	🍦🍦🍦🍦🍦🍦🍦

Each 🍦 = 2 votes

If 8 students voted for vanilla, how many ice cream cones will finish the graph?

Ⓕ 4   Ⓗ 6

Ⓖ 5   Ⓙ 8

5 Fran is making a picture graph to show how many apples she eats every week. Each symbol on her graph stands for 4 apples. If she eats 10 apples, how many symbols does she need to draw?

Ⓐ 2 and one half

Ⓑ 3

Ⓒ 3 and one half

Ⓓ 10

6 A camp counselor is making a picture graph to show how his students voted for their favorite hike in the Blue Ridge Mountains. What title would you choose for the picture graph? Explain why.

_____

_____

Lesson 4-12   Name _____

Brittany took a survey about the color of her friends' socks. The tally chart below shows the results.

Use the tally chart for 1 and 2.

Sock Colors

White	||||
Blue	|
Red	||

1   If the information on the tally chart was recorded on a bar graph, which colored sock would be represented by the longest bar?

Ⓐ White

Ⓑ Blue

Ⓒ Red

Ⓓ Blue & Red

2   According to the tally chart, how many friends in all did Brittany ask what color socks they were wearing?

Ⓕ 1

Ⓖ 2

Ⓗ 4

Ⓙ 7

Paul made the bar graph below to show the number of beach activities he saw people do during his one day trip to Cape Charles.

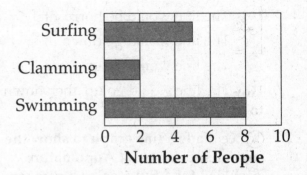

3   According to the bar graph, which was the most popular activity at Cape Charles?

Ⓐ Swimming

Ⓑ Clamming

Ⓒ Sunbathing

Ⓓ Surfing

4   What title would be most appropriate for the bar graph?

Ⓕ Swimming In Cape Charles

Ⓖ Favorite Activities At Cape Charles

Ⓗ Summer Time Activities

Ⓙ Things To Do In The Sun

5   Gina asked some students to choose their favorite breakfast. They chose cold cereal, waffles, pancakes, and oatmeal. If she makes a bar graph to show the data, how many bars will she need to make on the graph? How do you know?

_____

_____

Lesson 4-13   Name _____

1 Sarah made a line graph showing the changes in height of a student from age 5 to age 9. Which would MOST LIKELY describe the line?

  Ⓐ The line would be horizontal.

  Ⓑ The line would go down.

  Ⓒ The line would go up.

  Ⓓ The line would go up, then down.

2 Vince made a line graph to show the noon temperature at Appomattox each day for a full week. How many points will he draw on his graph?

  Ⓕ 2   Ⓗ 6

  Ⓖ 5   Ⓙ 7

3 Denise is making a line graph to show the number of books she has read. In October she read 7 books and in November she read 4 books. Which would describe the line from October to November on her graph?

  Ⓐ The line would be horizontal.

  Ⓑ The line would go down.

  Ⓒ The line would go up.

  Ⓓ The line would go up, then down.

4 Allie made a line graph showing the distance she jogged for 5 days. On Monday and Tuesday she jogged the same distance. Which would describe the line drawn from Monday to Tuesday?

  Ⓕ The line would be horizontal.

  Ⓖ The line would go down.

  Ⓗ The line would go up.

  Ⓙ The line would go up, then down.

5 Jesse recorded the number of miles he walked each week for 4 weeks in the chart shown below. Which graph shows this information?

Miles Walked

Week	1	2	3	4
Miles	4	6	5	8

Ⓐ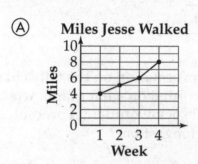

Ⓑ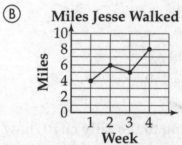

Ⓒ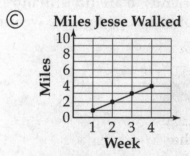

Ⓓ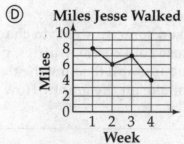

Lesson 4-14   Name _____

1 Whose class planted the most trees?

Students Planting Trees on Arbor Day	
Jack's Class	🌳🌳🌳
Abdul's Class	🌳🌳🌳🌳🌳🌳🌳🌳🌳
Lisa's Class	🌳🌳🌳🌳🌳
Yvonne's Class	🌳🌳🌳🌳🌳🌳

Each 🌳 = 2 trees.

Ⓐ Jack's   Ⓒ Lisa's

Ⓑ Abdul's   Ⓓ Yvonne's

2 Which sport did 4 more students choose than swimming?

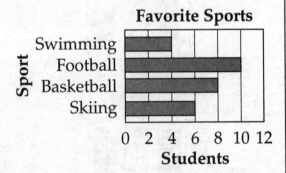

Favorite Sports

Ⓕ Football   Ⓗ Skiing

Ⓖ Basketball Ⓙ None

3 How many more students read 4 books than read 2 books?

Students
```
            X
        X   X
    X   X   X
    X   X   X   X
    X   X   X   X
    1   2   3   4   5   6
```
Number of Books Read

Ⓐ 2   Ⓒ 5

Ⓑ 3   Ⓓ 8

4 The bar graph below shows the favorite farm animals of children in a Staunton 4-H Club. How many children chose the cow and the horse in all?

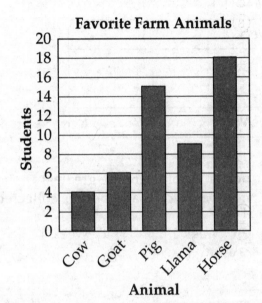

Favorite Farm Animals

Ⓕ 4   Ⓗ 20

Ⓖ 18   Ⓙ 22

5 Roger's class saw 25 butterflies in all. How many more butterflies should they put on the graph?

Students Spotting Butterflies	
Karen's Class	🦋🦋🦋🦋🦋🦋
Roger's Class	🦋🦋🦋
Melody's Class	🦋🦋🦋🦋🦋
Cliff's Class	🦋🦋🦋🦋

Each 🦋 = 5 butterflies.

Ⓐ 5   Ⓒ 2

Ⓑ 3   Ⓓ 1

Lesson 4-15   Name _____

Use the table for 1–2.

Bottle and Can Collection

Week	Number Collected
Week 1	18
Week 2	16
Week 3	13
Week 4	17
Week 5	7

1 Which week were the greatest number of cans and bottles collected?

  Ⓐ Week 1　　Ⓒ Week 4
  Ⓑ Week 2　　Ⓓ Week 5

2 How many more cans were collected in Week 2 than Week 5?

  Ⓕ 2　　Ⓗ 9
  Ⓖ 3　　Ⓙ 11

3 Renzo started along the Blue Ridge Highway at 8 A.M. He stopped at 1 P.M. How many hours did he ride?

  Ⓐ 9　　Ⓒ 6
  Ⓑ 7　　Ⓓ 5

4 On Monday, 286 students visited Mount Vernon. On Tuesday, 74 more students visited Mount Vernon than visited on Monday. How many students visited on Tuesday?

  Ⓕ 212　　Ⓗ 350
  Ⓖ 250　　Ⓙ 360

5 The table shows the times and the number of people who signed up for tours of a Newport News fire station.

Fire Station Tours

Time	Number of People
8:00	7
9:00	8
10:00	6

Which graph represents this data?

Ⓐ
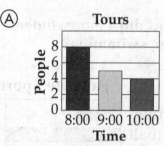

Ⓑ
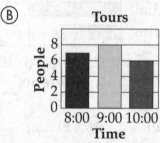

Ⓒ
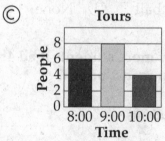

Ⓓ
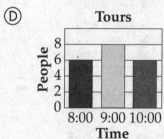

Lesson 5-1   Name _____

1   **Which shows 2 groups of 4?**

Ⓐ

Ⓑ

Ⓒ

Ⓓ

2   **Which sentence shows 5 groups of 2?**

Ⓕ $5 \times 2 = 10$ Ⓗ $5 - 2 = 3$

Ⓖ $5 + 2 = 7$ Ⓙ $5 \times 5 = 25$

3   **Which has the same value as**
     6 + 6 + 6?

Ⓐ 6×6 Ⓒ 1×6

Ⓑ 3×6 Ⓓ $3 + 6$

4   **Which number sentence describes**
     these sets of dots?

Ⓕ $5 + 3 = 8$ Ⓗ $5 \times 3 = 15$

Ⓖ $5 + 5 = 10$ Ⓙ $3 \times 3 = 9$

5   **Which has the same value as 8 + 8?**

Ⓐ 2×8 Ⓒ 4×8

Ⓑ 8×1 Ⓓ 8×8

6   **Which has the same value as**
     4 + 4 + 4 + 4 + 4?

Ⓕ $4 + 4 = 8$

Ⓖ $4 + 5 = 9$

Ⓗ $2 \times 5 = 10$

Ⓙ $5 \times 4 = 20$

7   **Which has the same value as 3 × 4?**

Ⓐ $3 + 3 + 3$

Ⓑ $4 + 3$

Ⓒ $4 + 4 + 4$

Ⓓ $4 + 3 + 3$

8   **Which number sentence describes**
     these sets of dots?

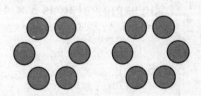

Ⓕ $2 \times 6 = 12$

Ⓖ $6 \times 1 = 6$

Ⓗ $2 \times 2 = 4$

Ⓙ $2 \times 1 = 2$

SOL 3.10 The student will represent multiplication … using … area models….
SOL 3.25a The student will investigate … relations that model the … commutative properties for … multiplication.

Lesson 5-2   Name _____

1 **What multiplication sentence should Sara write for this array?**

X X X X
X X X X
X X X X

(A) $2 \times 6 = 12$

(B) $4 \times 4 = 16$

(C) $3 \times 4 = 12$

(D) $3 \times 5 = 15$

2 **Which expression describes this array?**

☐ ☐ ☐ ☐ ☐ ☐
☐ ☐ ☐ ☐ ☐ ☐
☐ ☐ ☐ ☐ ☐

(F) $6 + 3$

(G) 3×6

(H) $3 + 6$

(J) $3 + 3 + 3 + 3$

3 **Which has the same value as 5×4?**

(A) $5 + 4$

(B) $5 + 5 + 5$

(C) $4 + 4$

(D) 4×5

4 **Which has the same product as 9×3?**

(F) 3×9 (H) $3 + 3 + 3$

(G) $3 + 9$ (J) 3×3

5 **Which multiplication sentence describes the array?**

● ● ● ●
● ● ● ●
● ● ● ●
● ● ● ●
● ● ● ●
● ● ● ●
● ● ● ●

(A) $6 \times 5 = 30$

(B) $7 \times 4 = 28$

(C) $7 + 4 = 11$

(D) $7 + 7 + 4 + 4 = 22$

6 **What is the product of 2×6?**

● ● ● ● ● ●
● ● ● ● ● ●

(F) 8

(G) 10

(H) 12

(J) 26

7 **Which array represents the product of 2×3?**

(A) ☐☐☐   (C) ☐☐
    ☐☐☐   ☐☐

(B) ☐☐☐☐   (D) ☐☐☐
    ☐☐☐☐   ☐☐☐
                   ☐☐☐

60

Lesson 5-3   Name _____

1 Amber has 3 ferrets. She bought 2 balls for each ferret.

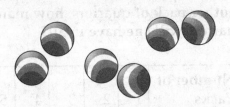

Which multiplication sentence shows how many balls she bought in all?

Ⓐ $2 + 2 = 4$

Ⓑ $2 \times 2 = 4$

Ⓒ $3 \times 1 = 3$

Ⓓ $3 \times 2 = 6$

2 There are 5 Virginia hams on each shelf in the store. There are 3 shelves.

Which multiplication sentence shows how many Virginia hams are on the shelves?

Ⓕ $3 \times 4 = 12$

Ⓖ $5 \times 2 = 10$

Ⓗ $3 \times 5 = 15$

Ⓙ $5 \times 5 = 25$

3 Mark bought 4 packs of tomatoes. There were 4 tomatoes in each pack. Which picture shows how to find the total number of tomatoes?

Ⓐ

Ⓑ

Ⓒ

Ⓓ

4 The trumpet players in the University of Virginia Marching Band are lined up in 3 rows of 6. Which number sentence describes how the trumpets are lined up?

Ⓕ $3 + 6$

Ⓖ $3 + 3 + 6 + 6$

Ⓗ 9×2

Ⓙ 3×6

5 Write a multiplication story for 2×7. Draw a picture to find the product.

_____

_____

Lesson 5-4   Name _____

1 Esther can put 5 apples in 1 basket. How many apples can she put in 5 baskets? Complete the table to solve the problem.

Baskets	1	2	3	4	5
Apples	5	10	15	?	?

(A) 5

(B) 15

(C) 20

(D) 25

2 Randy started doing pushups each day. The table shows the number of pushups he did each day for three days. If the pattern continues, how many pushups will he do on the sixth day?

Day	1	2	3	4	5	6
Pushups	4	8	12	?	?	?

(F) 24

(G) 16

(H) 12

(J) 6

3 Lea keeps her Virginia quarters in packs. The table shows how many packs of quarters she has. If she fills another pack of quarters, how many quarters will she have in all?

Number of Packs	1	2	3	4	5
Number of Quarters	8	16	24	32	?

(A) 5

(B) 37

(C) 40

(D) 56

4 It costs 6¢ a day for an overdue book at the library. Landon's book is 4 days overdue. How much is his fine for the overdue book?

Number of days	1	2	3	4
Fine	6¢	12¢	?	?

(F) 30¢   (H) 18¢

(G) 24¢   (J) 16¢

5 Marta made a table to find out how many model cars she can buy with $30. The model cars she wants cost $4 each. How many models can Marta buy? Explain how you got your answer.

Number of models	1	2	3	4	5	6	7	8
Cost	$4	$8	?	?	?	?	?	?

SOL 3.9 The student will recall the multiplication ... facts through the nines table.
SOL 3.10 The student will represent multiplication ..., using ... set models....
SOL 3.25a The student will investigate and create patterns involving numbers, [and] operations (... multiplication)....

Lesson 5-5   Name _____

1 $2 \times 4 =$ ☐

   Ⓐ 6

   Ⓑ 8

   Ⓒ 9

   Ⓓ 10

2   How many legs do 2 ants have?

   Ⓕ 2

   Ⓖ 6

   Ⓗ 10

   Ⓙ 12

3   Which is the product of 2 and 3?

   Ⓐ 6

   Ⓑ 5

   Ⓒ 4

   Ⓓ 3

4   Jan has 2 pockets. Each pocket has 1 penny. How many pennies does Jan have?

   Ⓕ 1

   Ⓖ 2

   Ⓗ 12

   Ⓙ 21

5   Kelly has 2 bags. Each bag has 7 balls. How many balls does Kelly have?

   Ⓐ 9

   Ⓑ 12

   Ⓒ 14

   Ⓓ 16

6   Multiply 2 times 2. The product is —

   Ⓕ 1

   Ⓖ 2

   Ⓗ 4

   Ⓙ 22

7   Mrs. Morales had 2 boxes of markers with 5 markers in each box. How many markers did she have altogether?

   Ⓐ 3

   Ⓑ 7

   Ⓒ 10

   Ⓓ 12

8   All multiples of 2 are even numbers. Which number below is not a multiple of 2?

   Ⓕ 18

   Ⓖ 15

   Ⓗ 14

   Ⓙ 2

SOL 3.9 The student will recall the multiplication ... facts through the nines table.
SOL 3.10 The student will represent multiplication ..., using area and set models....
SOL 3.25a The student will investigate ... patterns involving numbers, [and] operations (... multiplication)....

Lesson 5-6   Name _____

1 $5 \times 6 = \boxed{}$

   Ⓐ 11   Ⓒ 30

   Ⓑ 25   Ⓓ 35

2 What multiplication sentence is shown by the array of Virginia stickers below?

   Ⓕ $5 \times 4 = 20$

   Ⓖ $5 \times 5 = 25$

   Ⓗ $5 \times 6 = 30$

   Ⓙ $5 \times 7 = 35$

3 Which shows how to skip count to find 5×8?

   Ⓐ 5, 10, 15, 20

   Ⓑ 5, 10, 15, 20, 25, 30

   Ⓒ 5, 10, 15, 20, 30, 40

   Ⓓ 5, 10, 15, 20, 25, 30, 35, 40

4 Kayla has 3 nickels. Which multiplication sentence shows how much money she has?

   Ⓕ $3 \times 2 = 5$ cents

   Ⓖ $3 \times 5 = 8$ cents

   Ⓗ $3 \times 5 = 15$ cents

   Ⓙ $3 \times 5 = 20$ cents

5 Mr. Kelvin uses 5 grapes in each fruit salad. How many grapes will he need to make 4 fruit salads?

   Ⓐ 10

   Ⓑ 15

   Ⓒ 20

   Ⓓ 24

6 All multiples of 5 end in 0 or 5. Which number below is not a multiple of 5?

   Ⓕ 1

   Ⓖ 5

   Ⓗ 30

   Ⓙ 45

7
$$\begin{array}{r} 5 \\ \times\,2 \\ \hline \end{array}$$

   Ⓐ 7

   Ⓑ 10

   Ⓒ 15

   Ⓓ 20

8 What multiplication sentence is shown by the model below?

   Ⓕ $1 \times 5 = 5$

   Ⓖ $1 + 5 = 6$

   Ⓗ $1 \times 1 = 1$

   Ⓙ $5 \times 2 = 10$

64

Lesson 5-7

Name _____

1 $2 \times 10 = \square$

Ⓐ 12

Ⓑ 20

Ⓒ 22

Ⓓ 25

2 What is the next number in the pattern shown below?

10, 20, 30, 40, 50, 60, 70, 80, 90

Ⓕ 95

Ⓖ 98

Ⓗ 100

Ⓙ 170

3 Wanda skip counted 10, 20, 30, 40, 50, 60 to find a product. Which shows the product she found?

Ⓐ 5×5

Ⓑ 5×6

Ⓒ 5×10

Ⓓ 6×10

4 Kevin has 5 dimes. Which multiplication sentence shows how much money he has?

Ⓕ $5 \times 3 = 15$ cents

Ⓖ $5 \times 4 = 20$ cents

Ⓗ $5 \times 5 = 25$ cents

Ⓙ $5 \times 10 = 50$ cents

5 How many legs are on 10 horses?

Ⓐ 40   Ⓒ 60

Ⓑ 50   Ⓓ 70

6 Which number below is a multiple of 10?

Ⓕ 15   Ⓗ 35

Ⓖ 24   Ⓙ 50

7 $7 \times 10 = \square$

Ⓐ 80

Ⓑ 70

Ⓒ 60

Ⓓ 17

8 $\begin{array}{r} \$10 \\ \times\ 4 \\ \hline \end{array}$

Ⓕ $10

Ⓖ $20

Ⓗ $40

Ⓙ $50

9 Taylor has 8 packs of football cards. There are 10 cards in each pack. How many cards does he have?

Ⓐ 18

Ⓑ 80

Ⓒ 88

Ⓓ 108

Lesson 5-8   Name _____

1 Robin ordered 1 bagel and 3 hot chocolates. How much money will she need?

Snack	Price
Bagel	$4
Soft Pretzel	$3
Hot Chocolate	$2

Ⓐ $6

Ⓑ $9

Ⓒ $10

Ⓓ $14

2 James bought 2 packs of stickers. Each pack contained 5 stickers. He gave half of the stickers to his brother. How many stickers does James have left?

Ⓕ 3 stickers

Ⓖ 5 stickers

Ⓗ 7 stickers

Ⓙ 10 stickers

3 Mina bought 3 red balloons and 5 blue balloons for her party. The balloons cost 5¢ each. How much did Mina spend?

Ⓐ 13¢

Ⓑ 15¢

Ⓒ 25¢

Ⓓ 40¢

4 Berto ordered 2 slices of pizza and an apple juice. Each slice of pizza cost $3. The apple juice cost $2. How much did Berto spend?

Ⓕ $5

Ⓖ $6

Ⓗ $8

Ⓙ $9

5 Erin buys 4 bags of red apples and 1 bag of green apples. Each bag has 5 apples. How many apples does she buy?

Ⓐ 15

Ⓑ 20

Ⓒ 25

Ⓓ 30

6 Amos had 4 boxes. He put 5 paperweights in each box. Then he gave away 2 boxes. How many paperweights did he have left? Explain your answer using words, tables, diagrams, or pictures.

_____

Lesson 5-9   Name _____

1 What multiplication sentence is shown by the model below?

- Ⓐ $1 \times 1 = 1$
- Ⓑ $1 \times 4 = 4$
- Ⓒ $2 \times 2 = 4$
- Ⓓ $1 + 4 = 5$

2 $0 \times 6 = \square$

- Ⓕ 0
- Ⓖ 1
- Ⓗ 6
- Ⓙ 60

3 Beth buys 1 book of raffle tickets. There are 5 tickets in the book. How many raffle tickets does she buy?

- Ⓐ 0
- Ⓑ 1
- Ⓒ 5
- Ⓓ 6

4 $1 \times 7 = \square$

- Ⓕ 0
- Ⓖ 7
- Ⓗ 8
- Ⓙ 17

5 $3 \times 0 = \square$

- Ⓐ 30
- Ⓑ 10
- Ⓒ 3
- Ⓓ 0

6 When you multiply a number and 1, the product is that number. Which shows this property of multiplication?

- Ⓕ $0 \times 4 = 0$
- Ⓖ $2 \times 2 = 4$
- Ⓗ $1 \times 10 = 10$
- Ⓙ $5 \times 3 = 15$

7 There are 6 bowls on the table. There are no apples in the bowls. How many apples are there?

- Ⓐ 0
- Ⓑ 1
- Ⓒ 3
- Ⓓ 6

8 Which number makes the number sentence true?

$$9 \times \square = 9$$

- Ⓕ 0
- Ⓖ 1
- Ⓗ 9
- Ⓙ 10

Lesson 5-10   Name _____

1 $3 \times 9 = \boxed{}$

(A) 12

(B) 18

(C) 27

(D) 39

2   Multiply 9 and 2. The product is —

(F) 18

(G) 16

(H) 15

(J) 11

3   Which number makes the number sentence true?

$5 \times \boxed{} = 45$

(A) 5

(B) 9

(C) 45

(D) 54

4   Juan bought 9 packages of hamburger rolls. Each package has 6 rolls. How many rolls did he get?

(F) 15   (H) 54

(G) 36   (J) 63

5   Which is not a multiple of 9?

(A) 21

(B) 27

(C) 54

(D) 81

6 $\begin{array}{r} 9 \\ \times\,7 \\ \hline \end{array}$

(F) 69

(G) 63

(H) 54

(J) 16

7   Wan put 9 plates on the table. Each plate had 8 carrots. How many carrots were on the table?

(A) 17

(B) 63

(C) 70

(D) 72

8   What is the product of 9 and 9?

(F) 18

(G) 54

(H) 81

(J) 89

9   Carly used a pattern to find 4 × 9. Describe a pattern you can use to find 4 × 9.

_____

_____

Lesson 5-11   Name _____

1 $2 \times 5 = \boxed{}$

Ⓐ 7

Ⓑ 10

Ⓒ 12

Ⓓ 15

2 $0 \times 7 = \boxed{}$

Ⓕ 0

Ⓖ 1

Ⓗ 7

Ⓙ 17

3   There are 5 books on each shelf. The bookcase has 4 shelves. How many books are on the bookcase?

Ⓐ 9

Ⓑ 15

Ⓒ 20

Ⓓ 24

4   Travis has 1 bag of marbles. There are 8 marbles in the bag. How many marbles does Travis have?

Ⓕ 1

Ⓖ 8

Ⓗ 9

Ⓙ 18

5   Multiples of 5 must have a 0 or a 5 in the ones place. Which number below is a multiple of 5?

Ⓐ 8

Ⓑ 11

Ⓒ 32

Ⓓ 40

6   There are 6 vases. Each vase holds 2 roses. How many roses are there?

Ⓕ 6

Ⓖ 8

Ⓗ 12

Ⓙ 14

7 $9 \times 6 = \boxed{}$

Ⓐ 96

Ⓑ 63

Ⓒ 54

Ⓓ 45

8   The digits in products of multiples of 9 add up to 9. Which product below is not a multiple of 9?

Ⓕ 18

Ⓖ 36

Ⓗ 42

Ⓙ 63

SOL 3.8 The student will solve problems involving the sum or difference of two whole numbers, each 9,999 or less, with or without grouping, using various computational methods, including … paper and pencil … and estimation.
SOL 3.9 The student will recall the multiplication … facts through the nines table.

Lesson 5-12   Name _____

1 Ron passed 9 lawns on his way to school. He saw 2 pine trees in each lawn. How many pine trees did he see?

Ⓐ 9

Ⓑ 11

Ⓒ 16

Ⓓ 18

2 Andrew has 5 packs of trading cards. There are 6 cards in each pack. How many trading cards does Andrew have?

Ⓕ 11

Ⓖ 25

Ⓗ 30

Ⓙ 35

3 Jan has 35 white crystals and 28 pink crystals in her rock collection. How many crystals does she have in all?

Ⓐ 63

Ⓑ 53

Ⓒ 7

Ⓓ 6

4 Eric bought 2 packages of tapes with 6 tapes in each package. How many tapes did he buy?

Ⓕ 14

Ⓖ 12

Ⓗ 10

Ⓙ 8

5 James Madison was born in King George County, Virginia, in 1751. He died in 1836 and is buried at Montpelier Station, Virginia. How many years did James Madison live?

Ⓐ 25

Ⓑ 75

Ⓒ 85

Ⓓ 125

6 Annie ran 5 miles every day for 5 days. How many miles did she run in all?

Ⓕ 10

Ⓖ 15

Ⓗ 20

Ⓙ 25

7 The coach has 1 bag of soccer balls. There are 6 soccer balls in the bag. How many soccer balls are there?

Ⓐ 1

Ⓑ 6

Ⓒ 7

Ⓓ 60

8 Bryce rode his bike 9 miles each day for 7 days. How many miles did he ride in all?

Ⓕ 16

Ⓖ 56

Ⓗ 63

Ⓙ 72

Lesson 6-1   Name _____

1 Which expression describes the array?

● ● ● ● ●
● ● ● ● ●
● ● ● ● ●

Ⓐ 3 + 5

Ⓑ 3 + 3 + 3

Ⓒ 3 × 3

Ⓓ 3 × 5

2   4 × 3 =

Ⓕ 7

Ⓖ 8

Ⓗ 9

Ⓙ 12

3 Find the product of 3 and 1.

Ⓐ 2

Ⓑ 3

Ⓒ 4

Ⓓ 5

4   0
          × 3
          ———

Ⓕ 0

Ⓖ 1

Ⓗ 2

Ⓙ 3

5 There are 3 balls in each bag. How many balls are there in 2 bags?

Ⓐ 3

Ⓑ 5

Ⓒ 6

Ⓓ 9

6 What multiplication sentence should Mitch write for this array?

X X X
X X X
X X X

Ⓕ 2 × 3 = 6

Ⓖ 3 × 3 = 9

Ⓗ 3 × 4 = 12

Ⓙ 3 × 5 = 15

7 Which expression is not the same as

3 × 2?

Ⓐ 2 × 3

Ⓑ 2 × 2 × 2

Ⓒ 2 + 2 + 2

Ⓓ 3 + 3

8   7 × 3 =

Ⓕ 10

Ⓖ 18

Ⓗ 21

Ⓙ 24

71

SOL 3.9 The student will recall the multiplication ... facts through the nines table.
SOL 3.10 The student will represent multiplication... using area...models....

Lesson 6-2   Name _____

1 **Which expression describes the array?**

○ ○
○ ○

○ ○
○ ○

(A) 4 × 2

(B) 2 × 2

(C) 4 + 2

(D) 2 + 2

2   4 × 1 =

(F) 0

(G) 1

(H) 4

(J) 5

3 **Which 2s fact can you double to find the product of 4 × 6?**

(A) 2 × 1 = 2

(B) 2 × 2 = 4

(C) 2 × 4 = 8

(D) 2 × 6 = 12

4   4
    × 4
   ———

(F) 4

(G) 8

(H) 12

(J) 16

5 **Kate has 4 bunches of balloons. Each bunch has 7 balloons. How many balloons does Kate have?**

(A) 49

(B) 28

(C) 14

(D) 11

6 **What multiplication sentence should Travis write for this array?**

X X X X X
X X X X X
X X X X X
X X X X X

(F) 5 × 5 = 25

(G) 4 × 5 = 20

(H) 4 × 4 = 16

(J) 2 × 5 = 10

7 **Which expression is not the same as**

4 × 3?

(A) 3 × 4

(B) 3 × 3 × 3

(C) 3 + 3 + 3 + 3

(D) 4 + 4 + 4

8 **Haley bought 4 packages of CDs. Each package has 9 CDs in it. How many CDs does she have in all?**

(F) 12

(G) 32

(H) 36

(J) 40

Lesson 6-3   Name _____

1 Which multiplication sentence describes the array?

Ⓐ 5 × 4 = 20

Ⓑ 6 × 4 = 24

Ⓒ 5 × 5 = 25

Ⓓ 7 × 4 = 28

2   7 × 3 =

Ⓕ 11

Ⓖ 18

Ⓗ 21

Ⓙ 24

3   6 × 5 =

Ⓐ 11

Ⓑ 24

Ⓒ 30

Ⓓ 35

4 Leon saw 4 cardinals on each of the 7 days he visited his grandmother in Richmond. How many cardinals did Leon see in all?

Ⓕ 28

Ⓖ 24

Ⓗ 14

Ⓙ 11

5 Which fact below could you double to find 6 × 8?

Ⓐ 6 + 8 = 14

Ⓑ 2 × 6 = 12

Ⓒ 2 × 8 = 16

Ⓓ 3 × 8 = 24

6 What is the product of 7 and 9?

Ⓕ 16

Ⓖ 56

Ⓗ 59

Ⓙ 63

7 Draw a picture to show how to use 5s facts and 2s facts to find 7 × 4. Explain your drawing.

_____

_____

SOL 3.9 The student will recall the multiplication … facts through the nines table.
SOL 3.10 The student will represent multiplication … using area and set models….

Lesson 6-4

Name _____

1 **Which multiplication sentence describes the array?**

○ ○ ○ ○ ○ ○
○ ○ ○ ○ ○ ○
○ ○ ○ ○ ○ ○
○ ○ ○ ○ ○ ○
○ ○ ○ ○ ○ ○
○ ○ ○ ○ ○ ○
○ ○ ○ ○ ○ ○
○ ○ ○ ○ ○ ○

Ⓐ $7 \times 6 = 42$

Ⓑ $8 \times 6 = 48$

Ⓒ $8 \times 7 = 56$

Ⓓ $8 \times 8 = 64$

2 $8 \times 3 =$

Ⓕ 11   Ⓗ 21

Ⓖ 18   Ⓙ 24

3 $7 \times 8 =$

Ⓐ 56   Ⓒ 42

Ⓑ 54   Ⓓ 15

4 **Which expression is not the same as 8×5?**

Ⓕ 5×8

Ⓖ $8 \times 8 \times 8 \times 8 \times 8$

Ⓗ $8 + 8 + 8 + 8 + 8$

Ⓙ $5 + 5 + 5 + 5 + 5 + 5 + 5 + 5$

5 **Which fact below could you double to find 8×8?**

Ⓐ $8 + 8 = 16$

Ⓑ $3 \times 8 = 24$

Ⓒ $4 \times 8 = 32$

Ⓓ $5 \times 8 = 40$

6 $8 \times 9 =$

Ⓕ 17   Ⓗ 72

Ⓖ 64   Ⓙ 74

7 **Wendy used two arrays to find 8×4. What error did Wendy make? Fix her error and then give the correct answer.**

○ ○   ○ ○
○ ○   ○ ○
○ ○   ○ ○
○ ○   ○ ○

$4 \times 2 = 8$ $4 \times 2 = 8$

$8 + 8 = 16$

Lesson 6-5   Name _____

1 $3 \times 8 =$

Ⓐ 11
Ⓑ 21
Ⓒ 24
Ⓓ 27

2 $4 \times 7 =$

Ⓕ 11
Ⓖ 24
Ⓗ 26
Ⓙ 28

3 $\begin{array}{r} 9 \\ \times 2 \\ \hline \end{array}$

Ⓐ 11
Ⓑ 12
Ⓒ 16
Ⓓ 18

4 $0 \times 8 =$

Ⓕ 0
Ⓖ 8
Ⓗ 9
Ⓙ 10

5 $\begin{array}{r} 6 \\ \times 3 \\ \hline \end{array}$

Ⓐ 9
Ⓑ 12
Ⓒ 18
Ⓓ 21

6 $7 \times 7 =$

Ⓕ 14
Ⓖ 42
Ⓗ 48
Ⓙ 49

7 $8 \times 9 =$

Ⓐ 17
Ⓑ 64
Ⓒ 72
Ⓓ 74

8 $6 \times 7 =$

Ⓕ 49
Ⓖ 42
Ⓗ 36
Ⓙ 13

9 $\begin{array}{r} 5 \\ \times 8 \\ \hline \end{array}$

Ⓐ 45
Ⓑ 40
Ⓒ 35
Ⓓ 13

10 $9 \times 9 =$

Ⓕ 18
Ⓖ 64
Ⓗ 72
Ⓙ 81

SOL 3.24 The student will recognize and describe a variety of patterns formed using concrete objects, numbers, … and pictures, and extend the pattern, using the same or different forms (concrete objects, numbers, … and pictures).

Lesson 6-6   Name _____

1 What number should Derek write on the next card to follow the pattern?

- (A) 13
- (B) 15
- (C) 17
- (D) 19

2 In the pattern below, which number belongs in the box?

4, 8, 12, 16, ☐

- (F) 14
- (G) 18
- (H) 19
- (J) 20

3 What is the missing number that follows the pattern?

32, 28, 24, 20, ? , 12

- (A) 14
- (B) 16
- (C) 17
- (D) 18

4 Paloma painted a mural of dogwood trees to celebrate a local festival of the Virginia state tree and flower.

If the pattern continues, how many trees will be in the fourth row?

- (F) 11
- (H) 6
- (G) 10
- (J) 3

5 A pattern was used to determine the number of dark blocks and light blocks in each figure below.

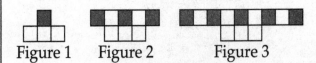

Figure 1   Figure 2   Figure 3

If the pattern continues, how many dark blocks will there be in Figure 5?

- (A) 5
- (C) 9
- (B) 7
- (D) 11

6 Sean made a design by drawing dots in boxes. Describe the pattern. How many dots will be in the next two boxes if the pattern continues?

76

Lesson 6-7   Name _____

1 Jenny has 5 blue balloons. Erin has twice as many red balloons. How many red balloons does Erin have?

Ⓐ 2

Ⓑ 3

Ⓒ 7

Ⓓ 10

2 Andrew is three times as old as Paul. Paul is 7. How old is Andrew?

Ⓕ 10

Ⓖ 18

Ⓗ 21

Ⓙ 24

3 Kayla painted 4 cards. Timothy painted 6 times as many cards. How many cards did Timothy paint?

Ⓐ 26

Ⓑ 24

Ⓒ 20

Ⓓ 10

4 Tyler rode his bike 5 miles. His big brother rode 7 times as far. How many miles did Tyler's brother ride?

Ⓕ 35

Ⓖ 30

Ⓗ 25

Ⓙ 12

5 Alexis has 9 marbles. Calvin has 4 times as many marbles. How many does Calvin have?

Ⓐ 14

Ⓑ 32

Ⓒ 36

Ⓓ 40

6 Justin did 8 pushups. Sue did twice as many. How many pushups did Sue do?

Ⓕ 10

Ⓖ 16

Ⓗ 20

Ⓙ 24

7 Alan read 9 pages. Clark read 3 times as many pages. How many pages did Clark read?

Ⓐ 27

Ⓑ 25

Ⓒ 21

Ⓓ 12

8 Natalie has 6 big shells in her shell collection. She has 7 times as many small shells. How many small shells are in Natalie's collection?

Ⓕ 13

Ⓖ 36

Ⓗ 40

Ⓙ 42

Lesson 6-8   Name _____

1 **Which fact do the shaded boxes in the multiplication table show how to find?**

X	0	1	2	3	4
0	0	0	0	0	0
1	0	1	2	3	4
2	0	2	4	6	8
3	0	3	6	9	12
4	0	4	8	12	16
5	0	5	10	15	20

Ⓐ $1 \times 4 = 4$

Ⓑ $5 \times 0 = 0$

Ⓒ $4 \times 4 = 16$

Ⓓ $5 \times 4 = 20$

2 **Fran finds $11 \times 3 = 33$ on a multiplication table. Use this fact to find 11×4.**

Ⓕ 34

Ⓖ 36

Ⓗ 44

Ⓙ 46

3 $7 \times 8 =$

Ⓐ 15

Ⓑ 56

Ⓒ 63

Ⓓ 64

4 **If $5 \times 12 = 60$, what should Dan add to 60 to find 12×6?**

Ⓕ 5

Ⓖ 6

Ⓗ 12

Ⓙ 60

5 **Which number is not in the 11s row on the multiplication table?**

Ⓐ 22

Ⓑ 33

Ⓒ 45

Ⓓ 55

6 $9 \times 6 =$

Ⓕ 56

Ⓖ 54

Ⓗ 48

Ⓙ 15

7 **Amanda explained how to use 11×6 to find 12×6. Explain how you could use an 11s fact to find 12×4.**

_____

_____

Lesson 6-9   Name _____

1 $3 \times 0 \times 4 =$

  (A) 0
  (B) 7
  (C) 4
  (D) 12

2 Roz has 2 bookcases. Each bookcase has 4 shelves. Each shelf has 2 trophies on it. How many trophies in all?

  (F) 8
  (G) 10
  (H) 16
  (J) 18

3 Ling has 4 pockets. Each pocket has 2 bags. Each bag has 4 marbles. How many marbles does Ling have?

  (A) 12
  (B) 18
  (C) 32
  (D) 44

4 $3 \times 2 \times 5 =$

  (F) 10
  (G) 11
  (H) 30
  (J) 40

5 Which product is the same as

$$2 \times 4 \times 3?$$

  (A) 8×2
  (B) 8×3
  (C) 8×4
  (D) 8×12

6 Which product is not the same as

$$6 \times 4 \times 2?$$

  (F) $(6 \times 4) \times 2$
  (G) $6 \times (4 \times 2)$
  (H) 24×12
  (J) $2 \times 4 \times 6$

7 Reed has 6 containers. Each container has 3 cups. Each cup has 1 pen. How many pens does Reed have?

  (A) 10
  (B) 18
  (C) 19
  (D) 20

8 $5 \times 4 \times 0 =$

  (F) 0
  (G) 9
  (H) 15
  (J) 20

Lesson 6-10   Name _____

1 **What is the rule used in this table?**

In	1	2	3	4	5
Out	6	12	18	24	30

Ⓐ Multiply by 4.

Ⓑ Multiply by 5.

Ⓒ Multiply by 6.

Ⓓ Multiply by 7.

2 **What is the rule used in the table below?**

In	3	4	5	6	7
Out	6	7	8	9	10

Ⓕ Add 2.

Ⓖ Add 3.

Ⓗ Add 4.

Ⓙ Add 5.

3 **What is the rule used in this table?**

Number of boxes	3	4	5	6	7
Number of fruit bars	24	32	40	48	56

Ⓐ Multiply by 5.

Ⓑ Multiply by 6.

Ⓒ Multiply by 7.

Ⓓ Multiply by 8.

4 **What are the missing numbers in the table below?**

In	5	6	7	8	9
Out	20	24	28	?	?

Ⓕ 10, 12

Ⓖ 29, 30

Ⓗ 30, 32

Ⓙ 32, 36

5 **What is the missing number in the table below?**

In	2	3	5	8
Out	14	21	35	?

Ⓐ 42

Ⓑ 49

Ⓒ 56

Ⓓ 70

6 **What is the missing number in this table?**

In	2	5	6	4	8
Out	16	40	48	32	?

Ⓕ 36

Ⓖ 42

Ⓗ 64

Ⓙ 72

SOL 3.8 The student will solve problems involving the … difference of two whole numbers, each 9,999 or less, with or without regrouping, using various computational methods…. **SOL 3.9** The student will recall the multiplication … facts through the nines table. **SOL 3.22** The student will read and interpret data represented in … bar graphs….

Lesson 6-11   Name _____

1 Brandon washed 5 cars last week. He spent 2 hours washing each car. How many hours did he wash the cars?

   Ⓐ 2   Ⓒ 10

   Ⓑ 7   Ⓓ 12

2 A chef made 34 sandwiches. Fifteen of the sandwiches were made with turkey. The rest were made with Virginia ham. How many Virginia ham sandwiches did the chef make?

   Ⓕ 19   Ⓗ 29

   Ⓖ 21   Ⓙ 49

3 The graph shows how long it took Gina to skate down some streets in her neighborhood.

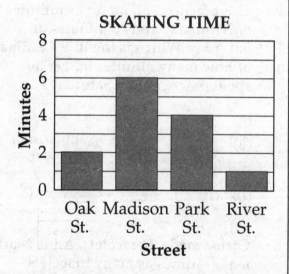

It took Gina 3 times as long to skate down Main Street as Park Street. How many minutes did it take her to skate down Main Street?

   Ⓐ 15   Ⓒ 9

   Ⓑ 12   Ⓓ 7

4 Leo earns $5 for an hour of yard work. How much will he earn if he does yard work for 3 hours?

   Ⓕ $8

   Ⓖ $11

   Ⓗ $15

   Ⓙ $18

5 The graph shows winter snowfall for three months in the Blue Ridge Mountains.

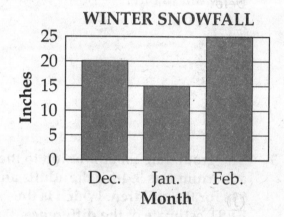

How many more inches of snow fell in December and January combined than in February?

   Ⓐ 10   Ⓒ 20

   Ⓑ 15   Ⓓ 35

6 Rachel spent 4 hours a day at the beach. How many hours did she spend at the beach in 6 days?

   Ⓕ 10

   Ⓖ 24

   Ⓗ 26

   Ⓙ 32

Lesson 6-12   Name _____

1 Mosi has 8 Mount Vernon stickers. He needs 3 times this many to make invitations for a 4th of July party. How many stickers does he need?

Ⓐ 11
Ⓑ 21
Ⓒ 24
Ⓓ 28

2 Jo bought twice as many pears as Roy. If Roy bought 4 pears, how many did Jo buy?

Ⓕ 6
Ⓖ 8
Ⓗ 12
Ⓙ 14

3 The group rate for admission to the aquarium was $91 for the adults and $48 for the children. Which is the BEST estimate of the difference between the adult and child rate?

Ⓐ $30
Ⓑ $40
Ⓒ $50
Ⓓ $60

4 There are 5 trains in each box. How many trains are in 7 boxes?

Ⓕ 35
Ⓖ 30
Ⓗ 25
Ⓙ 12

5 One bag of apples costs $3. How much does 6 bags of apples cost?

Ⓐ $9
Ⓑ $12
Ⓒ $15
Ⓓ $18

6 Whitney visited Monticello 7 times. Ms. Troy visited Monticello twice as often as Whitney. How many times did Ms. Troy visit Monticello?

Ⓕ 10
Ⓖ 12
Ⓗ 14
Ⓙ 16

7 Tim practiced piano for 19 minutes on Thursday and 48 minutes on Saturday. Which is the BEST estimate of how many minutes longer he spent practicing on Saturday?

Ⓐ 20
Ⓑ 30
Ⓒ 40
Ⓓ 60

8 Carlos made 9 bracelets. Anna Maria made 4 times as many bracelets. How many bracelets did Anna Maria make?

Ⓕ 13
Ⓖ 28
Ⓗ 32
Ⓙ 36

Lesson 7-1

Name _____

1 If 48 corn seeds are planted in 6 equal rows, how many corn seeds will be in each row?

(A) 6   (C) 24

(B) 8   (D) 288

2 A large pizza with 18 pieces is shared equally by 3 people. How many slices will each person get?

(F) 4   (H) 7

(G) 6   (J) 8

3 Ashley drew this picture to find out how many seashells each of her 4 friends would get if they shared 20 seashells equally.

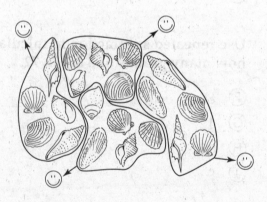

Which division number sentence below describes the problem?

(A) $20 \div 1 = 20$

(B) $20 \div 2 = 10$

(C) $20 \div 4 = 5$

(D) $20 \div 5 = 4$

4 Four friends equally shared the $36 they earned raking leaves. Which number sentence describes how they figured out how much each got to keep?

(F) $36 \div 4 = \$9$

(G) $36 \times 4 = \$144$

(H) $36 - 4 = \$32$

(J) $36 \div 3 = \$12$

5 In Virginia, Interstate 95 covers about 180 miles. The Chung family drove 60 miles per hour. How long did it take the family to cross Virginia on their way to Florida?

(A) 1 hour

(B) 2 hours

(C) 3 hours

(D) 4 hours

6 There are 15 markers to be equally shared among 5 students. How many markers will each student get?

(F) 6

(G) 5

(H) 4

(J) 3

Lesson 7-2   Name _____

1 Use repeated subtraction to calculate how many groups of 3 are in 27.

    Ⓐ 10

    Ⓑ 9

    Ⓒ 8

    Ⓓ 6

2 On a field trip to see Natural Bridge, Miss Kelly gave 4 cookies to each student on the bus. All 36 cookies were given out equally. How many students were there on the bus?

    Ⓕ 36

    Ⓖ 18

    Ⓗ 9

    Ⓙ 8

3 Corn can be planted in mounds or hills by placing 3 seeds in each hill. 24 corn seeds are planted in this way. Use repeated subtraction to figure out how many hills there are.

    Ⓐ 8 hills

    Ⓑ 12 hills

    Ⓒ 24 hills

    Ⓓ 27 hills

4 You have 56 books to put on shelves. Seven books fit on each shelf. How many shelves will you need?

    Ⓕ 10

    Ⓖ 8

    Ⓗ 6

    Ⓙ 4

5 At the Science Museum of Virginia, teachers divided 42 students into groups of 7 to see an exhibit. How many groups were there?

    Ⓐ 9

    Ⓑ 8

    Ⓒ 7

    Ⓓ 6

6 Use repeated subtraction to calculate how many groups of 8 are in 72.

    Ⓕ 80

    Ⓖ 12

    Ⓗ 11

    Ⓙ 9

7 Davis has 24 stickers that he wants to pass out equally to his friends. What different numbers of friends can he choose to pass the stickers out to? List all the possibilities.

_____

_____

Lesson 7-3   Name _____

1   Which division story explains the number sentence $63 \div 9 = \boxed{}$?

  Ⓐ A teacher equally divides 63 marbles among 9 students.

  Ⓑ A teacher gives 63 marbles to each of 9 students.

  Ⓒ A teacher equally divides 9 marbles among 63 students.

  Ⓓ A teacher gives 63 marbles to 9 students. They can each take as many as they want.

2   The third grade students are going on a field trip to Mount Vernon. If there are 64 students and 8 students in each group, how many groups are there?

  Ⓕ 6

  Ⓖ 7

  Ⓗ 8

  Ⓙ 72

3   The 42 students in a schoolyard form _____ rows with _____ students in each row. Which numbers complete the division story above?

  Ⓐ 6; 8

  Ⓑ 7; 6

  Ⓒ 9; 5

  Ⓓ 7; 7

4   Find the division story that matches the number sentence $20 \div 5 = \boxed{w}$.

  Ⓕ A bike trip of 20 miles takes more than 5 hours.

  Ⓖ The box of 20 crayons is evenly divided among 5 students.

  Ⓗ There are 5 cars going on a 20-hour drive to Alaska.

  Ⓙ If you earn $20 every day, then it will take 5 days to earn $100.

5   Farmer Joe has 35 pea seeds. He wants to plant them in rows with an equal number of seeds in each row and none left over. Explain the two ways that Joe can plant his peas.

_____

_____

Lesson 7-4   Name _____

1 Julia wants to buy a magazine that costs 57¢. Which combination of quarters, nickels and pennies will be enough to buy the magazine?

Ⓐ 2 quarters and 2 pennies

Ⓑ 1 quarter, 5 nickels and 2 pennies

Ⓒ 1 quarter, 6 nickels and 2 pennies

Ⓓ 1 quarter, 3 nickels and 12 pennies

2 Pedro has $25 to spend on toys. A set of blocks costs $6.39, a model car set costs $5.16, and a video game costs $8.96. If he buys one of each, how much money will he have left?

Ⓕ $20.51

Ⓖ $19.51

Ⓗ $5.49

Ⓙ $4.49

3 The drive from Richmond to Lynchburg takes about 2 hours. The drive from Lynchburg to Roanoke takes half as long. How long would it take to drive from Richmond to Roanoke through Lynchburg?

Ⓐ 1 hour   Ⓒ 3 hours

Ⓑ 2 hours   Ⓓ 4 hours

4 Estimate how long it would take to ride a horse from Richmond to Fredericksburg if it takes 45 minutes by car. A car is about 8 times faster than a horse over a long distance.

Ⓕ 6 minutes

Ⓖ 6 hours

Ⓗ 6 days

Ⓙ 6 weeks

5 The figure below shows locations Arch, Bog, Crater and Dump along a straight road. Use the facts below to calculate the missing distance.

Arch to Dump is 18 miles.

Arch to Bog is 7 miles.

Bog to Crater is 8 miles.

Crater to Dump is

_____

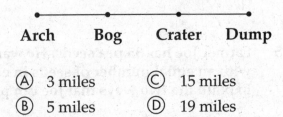

Arch   Bog   Crater   Dump

Ⓐ 3 miles   Ⓒ 15 miles

Ⓑ 5 miles   Ⓓ 19 miles

6 A farmer owns cows worth $300 each, pigs worth $200 each and sheep worth $100 each. Explain how many of each he could sell to raise $2,000. Give at least 2 different answers.

_____

_____

Lesson 7-5   Name _____

1 What number will complete the facts

$8 \times \boxed{} = 56$ and $56 \div 8 = \boxed{}$?

Ⓐ 6
Ⓑ 7
Ⓒ 8
Ⓓ 9

2 Which fact completes the fact family?

$4 \times 8 = 32$
$8 \times 4 = 32$
$32 \div 4 = 8$

Ⓕ $8 + 8 + 8 + 8 = 32$
Ⓖ $16 \times 2 = 32$
Ⓗ $32 \div 2 = 16$
Ⓙ $32 \div 8 = 4$

3 What number will complete the facts

$7 \times \boxed{} = 63$ and $63 \div \boxed{} = 7$?

Ⓐ 11
Ⓑ 10
Ⓒ 9
Ⓓ 8

4 What number will complete the facts

$72 \div \boxed{} = 8$ and $8 \times \boxed{} = 72$?

Ⓕ 6
Ⓖ 7
Ⓗ 8
Ⓙ 9

5 Which fact completes this fact family?

$9 \times 6 = 54$
$6 \times 9 = 54$
$54 \div 6 = 9$

Ⓐ $54 \div 3 = 18$
Ⓑ $18 \times 3 = 54$
Ⓒ $54 \div 9 = 6$
Ⓓ $54 + 6 = 60$

6 What multiplication fact can help you find $45 \div 9$?

Ⓕ $3 \times 15 = 45$
Ⓖ $5 \times 9 = 45$
Ⓗ $45 \div 5 = 9$
Ⓙ $45 \div 3 = 15$

7 What multiplication fact can help you find $81 \div 9$?

Ⓐ $81 \div 3 = 27$
Ⓑ $81 \div 27 = 3$
Ⓒ $9 \times 9 = 81$
Ⓓ $27 \times 3 = 81$

8 What multiplication fact can help you find $54 \div 9$?

Ⓕ $54 \div 6 = 9$
Ⓖ $54 \div 2 = 27$
Ⓗ $2 \times 27 = 54$
Ⓙ $6 \times 9 = 54$

SOL 3.4 The student will recognize and use the inverse relationships between … multiplication/division to complete basic fact sentences. The student will use these relationships to solve problems…. **SOL 3.9** The student will recall the … division facts through the nines table.

Lesson 7-6   Name _____

1   What multiplication expression can help you find 45 ÷ 5?

Ⓐ 5 × 8

Ⓑ 45 × 9

Ⓒ 5 × 9

Ⓓ 45 × 5

2   A large pizza with 30 pieces is being shared by 5 people. How many pieces will each person get?

Ⓕ 2

Ⓖ 3

Ⓗ 5

Ⓙ 6

3   Daniel bought a deck of 50 game cards. He gave 10 to his sister Evelyn and shared the rest equally with 4 of his friends. How many cards did Daniel and each of his friends end up with?

Ⓐ 1   Ⓒ 8

Ⓑ 5   Ⓓ 10

4   What multiplication expression can help you find 20 ÷ 2?

Ⓕ 9 × 2

Ⓖ 10 × 2

Ⓗ 11 × 2

Ⓙ 12 × 2

5   Juan equally divided his 18 baseball cards with his brother. How many cards did he give his brother?

Ⓐ 18

Ⓑ 12

Ⓒ 9

Ⓓ 6

6   John has 45¢ all in nickels. How many nickels does he have?

Ⓕ 3

Ⓖ 6

Ⓗ 9

Ⓙ 15

7   Which fact is not in the same fact family as 2 × 6 = 12?

Ⓐ 3 × 4 = 12

Ⓑ 12 ÷ 6 = 2

Ⓒ 12 ÷ 2 = 6

Ⓓ 6 × 2 = 12

8   Mrs. Boone has 2 bags with 10 apples in each. She gives an equal number of apples to her 5 children. How many apples does each child get?

Ⓕ 3

Ⓖ 4

Ⓗ 5

Ⓙ 10

Lesson 7-7   Name _____

1 If 3 students buy a large pizza for $12 and share the cost equally, how much will each pay?

Ⓐ $3

Ⓑ $4

Ⓒ $15

Ⓓ $36

2 What multiplication fact will help you find $36 \div 9$?

Ⓕ $6 \times 6 = 36$

Ⓖ $18 \times 2 = 36$

Ⓗ $9 \times 4 = 36$

Ⓙ $3 \times 12 = 36$

3 A geologist divides 20 pounds of rocks equally into 4 bags. What is the weight of the rocks in each bag?

Ⓐ 2 pounds

Ⓑ 4 pounds

Ⓒ 5 pounds

Ⓓ 24 pounds

4 If $36 \div 4$ is 9, what do you know about the quotient of $36 \div 3$?

Ⓕ It is less than 9.

Ⓖ It is 9.

Ⓗ It is greater than 9.

Ⓙ It is 13.

5 If $27 \div 3 = 9$, then $27 \div 9 = $?

Ⓐ 36

Ⓑ 30

Ⓒ 4

Ⓓ 3

6 Michael's family plans to drive from Richmond to the Grand Canyon in Arizona. They will take 4 days to do the 48 hours of driving needed to get there. They want to drive the same amount of time each day. How long will they drive each day?

Ⓕ 8 hours

Ⓖ 10 hours

Ⓗ 12 hours

Ⓙ 16 hours

7 If $72 \div 9 = 8$, then $72 \div 8 = $?

Ⓐ 7

Ⓑ 8

Ⓒ 9

Ⓓ 12

8 What multiplication fact will help you find $35 \div 7$?

Ⓕ $5 \times 5 = 25$

Ⓖ $5 \times 7 = 35$

Ⓗ $35 \div 5 = 7$

Ⓙ $35 - 7 = 28$

Lesson 7-8   Name _____

1 **Which fact is not in the same fact family as $6 \times 8 = 48$?**

   (A) $48 \div 6 = 8$

   (B) $8 \times 6 = 48$

   (C) $48 \div 8 = 6$

   (D) $48 \div 3 = 16$

2 **Which multiplication fact can help you find $54 \div 6$?**

   (F) $3 \times 18 = 54$

   (G) $6 \times 9 = 54$

   (H) $7 \times 8 = 56$

   (J) $8 \times 8 = 64$

3 **On a field trip to Richmond, Sally's class of 28 children had to ride in vans that held 7 children plus the driver. How many vans were needed?**

   (A) 7 vans

   (B) 5 vans

   (C) 4 vans

   (D) 3 vans

4 **The physical education teacher has 42 students in her class. How many volleyball teams, with 7 students on each team, can she make?**

   (F) 5

   (G) 6

   (H) 7

   (J) 8

5 **Casey ran a mile along Virginia Beach every day for 35 days. How many weeks was this?**

   (A) 5

   (B) 7

   (C) 40

   (D) 42

6 **Ms. Ruiz spent a 21 day business trip in Richmond. How many weeks was this?**

   (F) 2

   (G) 3

   (H) 7

   (J) 8

7 **Write the fact family for 7, 9, and 63.**

_____

_____

_____

_____

Lesson 7-9   Name _____

1 What multiplication fact can help you find $63 \div 9$?

(A) $9 \times 8 = 72$

(B) $8 \times 8 = 64$

(C) $7 \times 8 = 56$

(D) $7 \times 9 = 63$

2 Which fact is not in the same fact family as $72 \div 8 = 9$?

(F) $72 \div 9 = 8$

(G) $81 \div 9 = 9$

(H) $8 \times 9 = 72$

(J) $9 \times 8 = 72$

3 At a party, 8 friends equally shared the cost of Chinese takeout. The meal cost $32. How much did each person pay?

(A) $3

(B) $4

(C) $8

(D) $40

4 Katie has 54 corn seeds and wants to plant 9 seeds in each row. How many rows will she be able to plant?

(F) 8 rows

(G) 7 rows

(H) 6 rows

(J) 5 rows

5 On Monday Jason brought 2 bags of 12 cookies to his class. The teacher distributed the cookies equally to the 8 children in the class (including Jason). How many cookies did each child get?

(A) $1\frac{1}{2}$

(B) 2

(C) 3

(D) 4

6 On a bike ride, Jeremy's speedometer showed that he was only going 8 miles per hour. How long would it take him to complete a 56 mile bike ride at that speed?

(F) 9 hours

(G) 8 hours

(H) 7 hours

(J) 6 hours

7 The perimeter or distance around an octagon is 72 cm. If each side is the same length how long is a side?

(A) 6 cm

(B) 8 cm

(C) 9 cm

(D) 12 cm

Lesson 7-10   Name _____

1   Find the quotient.

$$3 \div 0 =$$

Ⓐ 0

Ⓑ 1

Ⓒ 3

Ⓓ Cannot be done

2   Find the quotient.

$$2{,}354 \div 1$$

Ⓕ 0

Ⓖ 1

Ⓗ 2,354

Ⓙ Cannot be done

3   The teacher brings in 2 bags containing 12 apples each. She distributes the apples equally among the 24 children in her class. How many apples does each child get?

Ⓐ 4

Ⓑ 3

Ⓒ 2

Ⓓ 1

4   Which number makes the number sentence true?

$$28 \div \boxed{} = 28$$

Ⓕ 0

Ⓖ 1

Ⓗ 28

Ⓙ Cannot be done

5   Which number makes the number sentence true?

$$0 \times \boxed{} = 16$$

Ⓐ 0

Ⓑ 1

Ⓒ 16

Ⓓ Cannot be done

6   Which fact is not in the same fact family as $8 \div 1 = 8$?

Ⓕ $0 \div 8 = 0$

Ⓖ $8 \div 8 = 1$

Ⓗ $8 \times 1 = 8$

Ⓙ $1 \times 8 = 8$

7   Find the quotient.

$$0 \div 7$$

Ⓐ 7

Ⓑ 1

Ⓒ 0

Ⓓ Cannot be done

8   How many times will zero divide into 9?

Ⓕ Cannot be done

Ⓖ 0

Ⓗ 9

Ⓙ 90

Lesson 7-11   Name _____

1 Which division story BEST explains the number sentence $75 \div 9 = \boxed{}$?

   Ⓐ A teacher equally divides 75 pencils among 9 students with none leftover.

   Ⓑ A teacher gives 9 pencils to each of 8 students with none left over.

   Ⓒ A teacher gives 9 pencils to each of 8 students and has 4 left over.

   Ⓓ A teacher gives 8 pencils to each of 9 students and has 3 left over.

2 Which **best describes** the number of weeks in 60 days?

   Ⓕ Exactly 8 weeks

   Ⓖ 8 weeks and 6 days

   Ⓗ 8 weeks and 4 days

   Ⓙ Exactly 9 weeks

3 If your lawn is 28 feet long, which **best describes** the length of your lawn in yards?

   Ⓐ Exactly 10 yards

   Ⓑ 9 yards and 2 feet

   Ⓒ 9 yards and 1 foot

   Ⓓ Exactly 9 yards

4 How many gallons of milk do you have if you buy 10 quarts?

1 gallon = 4 quarts

   Ⓕ Exactly 2 gallons

   Ⓖ 2 gallons and 2 quarts

   Ⓗ 3 gallons and 1 quart

   Ⓙ Exactly 3 gallons

5 If you divide a number GREATER THAN 6 by 6 what is the greatest number that can be left over?

   Ⓐ 3

   Ⓑ 4

   Ⓒ 5

   Ⓓ 6

6 The remainder is always —

   Ⓕ more than the divisor

   Ⓖ less than the divisor

   Ⓗ equal to the divisor

   Ⓙ more than the dividend

7 The drive from Richmond to Salt Lake City, Utah takes about 44 hours at 50 mph. Tim's family decides to drive only 8 hours every day. How many days will the trip take? How far will they have driven when they finally reach Salt Lake City?

_____

_____

Lesson 7-12   Name _____

1 How many dimes are needed to make $1.20?

Ⓐ 120

Ⓑ 12

Ⓒ 11

Ⓓ 10

2 The money used by the European Union, the euro, has an exchange rate of about 1 euro = $1.10, or 10 euros = $11. How many euros will you get if you go to France and buy euros with $132?

Ⓕ 12 euros

Ⓖ 13 euros

Ⓗ 110 euros

Ⓙ 120 euros

3 On Wednesday, farmer Jim sold 60 eggs. How many dozen eggs did he sell?

Ⓐ 1 dozen

Ⓑ 2 dozen

Ⓒ 5 dozen

Ⓓ 6 dozen

4 There are 70 bales of hay to gather. Jane can gather 10 bales of hay per hour. How long will it take her to gather the hay?

Ⓕ 6 hours

Ⓖ 7 hours

Ⓗ 9 hours

Ⓙ 10 hours

5 Find the quotient.

$$33 \div 11$$

Ⓐ 2

Ⓑ 3

Ⓒ 11

Ⓓ 22

6 Yolanda is planting 12 pea seeds in each row in her garden. If she plants 144 seeds, how many rows of peas will she have?

Ⓕ 72

Ⓖ 15

Ⓗ 14

Ⓙ 12

7 Frank withdrew $30 from his bank account. He received only ten-dollar bills. How many ten-dollar bills did he get?

Ⓐ 3,000

Ⓑ 300

Ⓒ 30

Ⓓ 3

8 Mr. Li bought 11 bouquets of flowers for his restaurant. He paid $99. How much did each bouquet cost him?

Ⓕ $8

Ⓖ $9

Ⓗ $10

Ⓙ $11

Lesson 7-13   Name _____

1 Which expression represents the word phrase, "the product of 9 and 3"?

Ⓐ 9 + 3

Ⓑ 9 × 3

Ⓒ 9 − 3

Ⓓ 9 ÷ 3

2 Which expression represents the word phrase, "36 apples shared equally by 9 people"?

Ⓕ 36 × 9

Ⓖ 36 + 9

Ⓗ 36 − 9

Ⓙ 36 ÷ 9

3 Which sentence would match the expression (2 × 12) ÷ 10?

Ⓐ Two groups of 10 children share 12 donuts.

Ⓑ Two dozen donuts were shared equally by 10 children with none leftover.

Ⓒ Two dozen donuts were shared equally by 10 children; 2 were left over.

Ⓓ Two dozen donuts were shared equally by 10 children; 4 were left over.

4 Choose the expression that matches the situation. "Matthew picked 54 bushels of apples each day for 9 days."

Ⓕ 54 ÷ 9   Ⓗ 54 − 9

Ⓖ 54 × 9   Ⓙ 54 + 9

5 Choose the expression that BEST matches the situation. "The 3 children earned $24 selling lemonade. $9 was owed for cups, sugar and lemons. The rest was shared by the 3 children."

Ⓐ 24 ÷ 3 − 9

Ⓑ 24 − 9 ÷ 3

Ⓒ (24 − 9) ÷ 3

Ⓓ 24 − 9 × 3

6 Choose the expression that matches the situation. "The ruler was divided into 3 equal parts."

Ⓕ 6 − 3

Ⓖ 6 × 3

Ⓗ 6 ÷ 3

Ⓙ 6 + 3

7 Choose the expression that BEST matches the situation. "Tora spent twice as long at Williamsburg as her brother did. Her brother spent 4 hours."

Ⓐ 4 ÷ 2

Ⓑ 4 + 2

Ⓒ 4 − 2

Ⓓ 4 × 2

SOL 3.8 The student will solve problems involving the sum ... of two whole numbers, each 9,999 or less, with or without regrouping, using various computational methods, including calculators, paper and pencil, mental computation, and estimation.
SOL 3.9 The student will recall the ... division facts through the nines table.

Lesson 7-14   Name _____

1   Sarah has $5.69 in change. If she has 9 quarters, 12 dimes and 37 nickels, how many pennies must she have?

(A) 14

(B) 39

(C) 54

(D) 69

2   A certain type of barn holds 5 horses comfortably. How many barns of this type are needed for 23 horses?

(F) 4

(G) 5

(H) 6

(J) 7

3   In Dungannon, farmer Warren plans to sell 95 organic seedlings at 5 for $1. Which expression shows how much money he will earn?

(A) 95 × $5

(B) 95 × $1

(C) 95 ÷ 5

(D) 95 ÷ 6

4   Josh's 3rd grade class is having a can-and-bottle drive. How many cans and bottles, worth 5 cents each, must they collect in order to raise a quarter?

(F) 5

(G) 10

(H) 15

(J) 20

5   Josh is driving from Maryland to Norfolk, Virginia. His entire trip will be 100 miles. Of that 100 miles 23 miles will be on the Chesapeake Bay Bridge-Tunnel. How many miles will not be on the bridge-tunnel?

(A) 123

(B) 87

(C) 77

(D) 67

6   Estimate the sum of 6,982 + 3,087 to the nearest thousand.

(F) 4,000

(G) 9,000

(H) 10,000

(J) 11,000

7   The Confederation Bridge linking Prince Edward Island to mainland Canada was completed in 1997. It took 42 months to build. How many years was this? How many extra months?

_____   _____

SOL 3.18 The student will analyze ... three-dimensional (solid) geometric figures (... cube, rectangular solid [prism], square pyramid, sphere, cone, and cylinder) and identify relevant properties ... using concrete models.

Lesson 8-1   Name _____

1 A drinking glass is most like what kind of solid figure?

(A) Cone   (C) Sphere

(B) Cube   (D) Cylinder

2 A refrigerator is most like what kind of solid figure?

(F) Cylinder

(G) Cube

(H) Rectangular prism

(J) Pyramid

3 A flagpole is most like what kind of solid figure?

(A) Cone

(B) Cylinder

(C) Pyramid

(D) Rectangular prism

4 What solid figures do you get if you break a cube in half?

(F) Two cubes

(G) Two pyramids

(H) Two rectangular prisms

(J) Two cylinders

5 A door is what kind of solid figure?

(A) Cube

(B) Cylinder

(C) Rectangular prism

(D) Pyramid

6 A tall tree that comes to a point at the top resembles what kind of solid figure?

(F) Cone

(G) Cylinder

(H) Pyramid

(J) Rectangular prism

SOL 3.18 The student will analyze ... three-dimensional (solid) geometric figures (... cube, rectangular solid [prism], square pyramid, sphere, cone, and cylinder) and identify relevant properties, including the number of corners, ... edges, and the number and shape of faces, using concrete models.

Lesson 8-2   Name _____

1   What solid figure has only one vertex?

(A) Pyramid

(B) Cone

(C) Sphere

(D) Cylinder

2   What solid figure has 8 edges?

(F)

(G)

(H)

(J)

3   How many faces does this pyramid have?

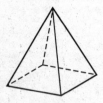

(A) 3 faces

(B) 4 faces

(C) 5 faces

(D) 6 faces

4   Which solid figure has edges that are all the same length?

(F)

(G)

(H)

(J)

5   What solid figure has only one face?

(A) Cone

(B) Cylinder

(C) Sphere

(D) Cube

6   What shape are the faces of a cylinder?

(F) Square

(G) Rectangle

(H) Triangle

(J) Circle

SOL 3.24 The student will recognize and describe a variety of patterns formed using concrete objects, numbers, ... and pictures, and extend the pattern, using the same or different forms (concrete objects, numbers, ... and pictures).

Lesson 8-3   Name _____

1   A pattern is built with cubes. The first item is 1 cube. The second item is a block of 8 cubes. The third item is a block of 27 cubes. If the pattern is continued, how many cubes are needed for the fourth and fifth items?

   Ⓐ   16, 25

   Ⓑ   48, 75

   Ⓒ   64, 125

   Ⓓ   80, 150

2   Every month a grocery store in Richmond has a "buy 1, get 2 free" sale. If you buy 2 items, you get 4 free. How many items would you come home with if you bought 4 items?

   Ⓕ   4

   Ⓖ   12

   Ⓗ   8

   Ⓙ   16

3   Andrew and Jessica counted their steps while walking to school. They noticed that for every 2 steps Andrew took, Jessica took 3 steps. When Andrew got to school he had taken 600 steps. How many steps did Jessica take to get to school?

   Ⓐ   400

   Ⓑ   600

   Ⓒ   800

   Ⓓ   900

4   Chris, Matt, Ashley and Sarah were standing in line. Chris was between Sarah and Ashley. Matt was in front of Ashley. Who was last in line?

   Ⓕ   Chris

   Ⓖ   Ashley

   Ⓗ   Sarah

   Ⓙ   Matt

5   A store clerk is building a tower of soup cans.
The bottom layer has 6 × 6 = 36 cans; the next layer has 5 × 5 = 25 cans; etc.
How many layers will the pyramid have when it is done?

_____

How many cans will be used? _____

Lesson 8-4   Name _____

1 How many times does a pair of parallel lines intersect?

   Ⓐ Never

   Ⓑ 1 time

   Ⓒ 2 times

   Ⓓ 3 times

2 Railroad tracks are an example of —

   Ⓕ intersecting lines

   Ⓖ intersecting rays

   Ⓗ parallel lines

   Ⓙ two points

3 Michael drew a line segment. Which would be Michael's drawing?

   Ⓐ

   Ⓑ

   Ⓒ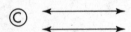

   Ⓓ

4 A part of a line with an endpoint on each end is called a —

   Ⓕ line

   Ⓖ line segment

   Ⓗ point

   Ⓙ ray

5 What is the name for this drawing?

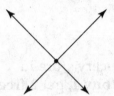

   Ⓐ Intersecting line segments

   Ⓑ Parallel lines

   Ⓒ Intersecting lines

   Ⓓ Intersecting rays

6 A part of a line that has one endpoint and is endless in one direction is called a —

   Ⓕ line

   Ⓖ line segment

   Ⓗ point

   Ⓙ ray

7 Draw and label an example of each of the following.

point

ray

line segment

line

Lesson 8-5   Name _____

1 An obtuse angle has a measure —

Ⓐ greater than a right angle

Ⓑ less than a right angle

Ⓒ the same as a right angle

Ⓓ the same as a straight line

2 At exactly 3 o'clock, what angle is made by the hands of a clock?

Ⓕ Obtuse

Ⓖ Acute

Ⓗ Right

Ⓙ No angle

3 At exactly 12 noon, what angle is made by the hands of a clock?

Ⓐ Obtuse

Ⓑ Acute

Ⓒ Right

Ⓓ No angle

4 What type of angle is shown?

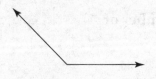

Ⓕ Obtuse

Ⓖ Acute

Ⓗ Right

Ⓙ No angle

5 What type of angle is formed inside the letter V?

Ⓐ Obtuse

Ⓑ Acute

Ⓒ Right

Ⓓ No angle

6 What angle is made by the borders of Virginia with Kentucky and Tennessee?

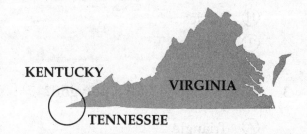

Ⓕ Obtuse

Ⓖ Acute

Ⓗ Right

Ⓙ No angle

7 What type of angle is formed by perpendicular lines?

Ⓐ Obtuse

Ⓑ Acute

Ⓒ Right

Ⓓ No angle

Lesson 8-6   Name _____

1 A polygon with 4 sides is called a —

   Ⓐ triangle

   Ⓑ quadrilateral

   Ⓒ pentagon

   Ⓓ hexagon

2 How many sides does an octagon have?

   Ⓕ 5 sides

   Ⓖ 6 sides

   Ⓗ 7 sides

   Ⓙ 8 sides

3 Which shape is not a polygon?

   Ⓐ Triangle

   Ⓑ Square

   Ⓒ Sphere

   Ⓓ Hexagon

4 The figure shown is which polygon?

   Ⓕ Triangle

   Ⓖ Quadrilateral

   Ⓗ Pentagon

   Ⓙ Hexagon

5 The figure shown is which polygon?

   Ⓐ Triangle

   Ⓑ Quadrilateral

   Ⓒ Pentagon

   Ⓓ Hexagon

6 Draw a quadrilateral. Write the number of sides and number of angles.

Lesson 8-7   Name _____

1   **A triangle that has 3 equal sides is —**

    Ⓐ   isosceles

    Ⓑ   scalene

    Ⓒ   equilateral

    Ⓓ   obtuse

2   **A triangle that has 2 equal sides is —**

    Ⓕ   isosceles

    Ⓖ   scalene

    Ⓗ   equilateral

    Ⓙ   obtuse

3   **A triangle that has 3 sides all different lengths is —**

    Ⓐ   isosceles

    Ⓑ   scalene

    Ⓒ   equilateral

    Ⓓ   obtuse

4   **An equilateral triangle always has —**

    Ⓕ   a right angle

    Ⓖ   all acute angles

    Ⓗ   an obtuse angle

    Ⓙ   only 2 acute angles

5   **Which triangle is obtuse?**

    Ⓐ

    Ⓑ 

    Ⓒ 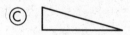

    Ⓓ 

6   **Which statement is false?**

    Ⓕ   A right triangle always has 2 acute angles.

    Ⓖ   An isosceles triangle always has 2 sides the same length.

    Ⓗ   An obtuse triangle always has 2 angles that are acute.

    Ⓙ   A scalene triangle cannot be an obtuse triangle.

7   **Which statement is false?**

    Ⓐ   An equilateral triangle is also isosceles.

    Ⓑ   An equilateral triangle is also acute.

    Ⓒ   An equilateral triangle is also obtuse.

    Ⓓ   An equilateral triangle has three sides of the same length.

Lesson 8-8   Name _____

1 **Which of these polygons is a quadrilateral?**

Ⓐ

Ⓑ

Ⓒ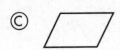

Ⓓ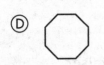

2 **A quadrilateral in which opposite sides are parallel and all sides have the same length is called a —**

Ⓕ parallelogram
Ⓖ trapezoid
Ⓗ rhombus
Ⓙ rectangle

3 **Which statement is false?**

Ⓐ A square is a rectangle.
Ⓑ A rectangle is a parallelogram.
Ⓒ A trapezoid is a parallelogram.
Ⓓ A rhombus is a parallelogram.

4 **What is the name of this quadrilateral?**

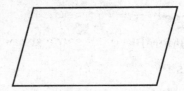

Ⓕ Parallelogram
Ⓖ Square
Ⓗ Rectangle
Ⓙ Trapezoid

5 **A trapezoid is a type of quadrilateral that has —**

Ⓐ two pairs of parallel sides
Ⓑ only one pair of parallel sides
Ⓒ all sides the same length
Ⓓ four right angles

6 **What is the name of this quadrilateral?**

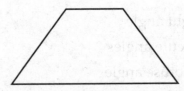

Ⓕ Parallelogram
Ⓖ Square
Ⓗ Rectangle
Ⓙ Trapezoid

Lesson 8-9   Name _____

1 When two figures are congruent it means that —

Ⓐ they only have the same size

Ⓑ they only have the same shape

Ⓒ they are right next to each other

Ⓓ they have the same size and shape

2 How has the original figure been moved to form the new figure?

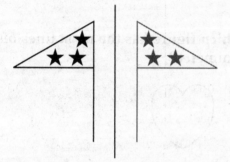

Ⓕ Turn

Ⓖ Flip

Ⓗ Slide

Ⓙ Turn and slide

3 Which figure is congruent to Figure 1?

Figure 1

Ⓐ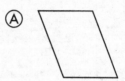

Ⓑ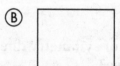

Ⓒ

Ⓓ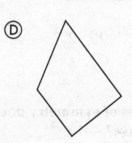

4 Another word for slide is —

Ⓕ translate   Ⓗ flip

Ⓖ rotate   Ⓙ turn

5 Draw a polygon. Then draw the same polygon after you flip it and then slide it.

SOL 3.20 The student, given appropriate drawings or models, will identify and describe ... symmetrical, two-dimensional (plane) figures, using tracing procedures.

Lesson 8-10   Name _____

1 How many lines of symmetry does the equilateral triangle have?

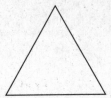

(A) None

(B) 1

(C) 2

(D) 3

2 How many lines of symmetry does this rectangle have?

(F) None   (H) 2

(G) 1   (J) 4

3 How many lines of symmetry does the letter 'H' have?

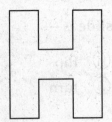

(A) None   (C) 2

(B) 1   (D) 3

4 How many lines of symmetry does the hexagon have?

(F) 8

(G) 6

(H) 5

(J) 4

5 Which figure has the most lines of symmetry?

(A)

(B)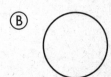

(C)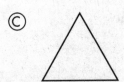

(D)

© Pearson Education, Inc. 3

Lesson 8-11   Name _____

1 **How do you find the perimeter of a figure?**

Ⓐ Count the number of squares inside.

Ⓑ Count the number of sides.

Ⓒ Find the total distance around the edges.

Ⓓ Multiply total distance around the edges by the number of sides.

2 **What is the perimeter of the triangle?**

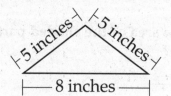

Ⓕ 40 square inches

Ⓖ 18 square inches

Ⓗ 18 inches

Ⓙ 13 inches

3 **What is the perimeter of the rectangle?**

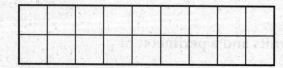

Ⓐ 11 units

Ⓑ 18 units

Ⓒ 20 units

Ⓓ 22 units

4 **Sarah measured one side of the hexagon. It was 3 centimeters long.**

If all sides are the same length, what is the perimeter of the hexagon?

Ⓕ 12 centimeters

Ⓖ 15 centimeters

Ⓗ 18 centimeters

Ⓙ 24 centimeters

5 **A football field is 120 yards long by 53 yards wide. If the coach makes the players run around the field twice, how far do they run?**

Ⓐ 173 yards

Ⓑ 346 yards

Ⓒ 519 yards

Ⓓ 692 yards

6 **What is the perimeter of an octagon if all sides are 5 inches long?**

Ⓕ 50 inches

Ⓖ 40 inches

Ⓗ 30 inches

Ⓙ 25 inches

Lesson 8-12   Name _____

1 **How do you find the area of a figure?**

Ⓐ Count the number of squares inside.

Ⓑ Count the number of sides.

Ⓒ Measure the total distance around the edges.

Ⓓ Multiply total distance around the edges by the number of sides.

2 **What is the area of the shaded part of the figure?**

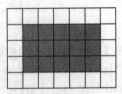

Ⓕ 8 square units

Ⓖ 15 square units

Ⓗ 16 square units

Ⓙ 35 square units

3 **What is the area and perimeter of the shaded part of the figure?**

Ⓐ 20 square units; 13 units

Ⓑ 13 square units; 18 units

Ⓒ 13 square units; 20 units

Ⓓ 15 square units; 20 units

4 **What is the area of the shaded part of this figure?**

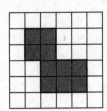

Ⓕ 18 square units

Ⓖ 16 square units

Ⓗ 12 square units

Ⓙ 10 square units

5 A rectangular garden has a length of 5 units and a perimeter of 16 units. Draw a diagram of the garden.

Find the width and the area of the garden.

_____

_____

Lesson 8-13   Name _____

1 **How do you find the volume of a solid figure?**

  Ⓐ Count the number of square units on the outside surface.

  Ⓑ Count the number of cubic units on the outside surface.

  Ⓒ Count the number of cubic units needed to fill the solid figure.

  Ⓓ Multiply the lengths of all the edges.

2 **Find the volume of this figure.**

  Ⓕ 6 cubic units

  Ⓖ 8 cubic units

  Ⓗ 10 cubic units

  Ⓙ 12 cubic units

3 **Jessica made a rectangular prism with 9 layers of cubes. There are 8 cubes in each layer. What is the volume of the rectangular prism?**

  Ⓐ 80 cubes

  Ⓑ 72 cubes

  Ⓒ 64 cubes

  Ⓓ 56 cubes

4 **Chris built a solid pillar using bricks. The pillar was 8 bricks long, 6 bricks wide and 10 bricks high. How many bricks were used to make the pillar?**

  Ⓕ 48 bricks

  Ⓖ 60 bricks

  Ⓗ 80 bricks

  Ⓙ 480 bricks

5 **A cord of firewood has a volume of 128 cubic feet. A pile 4 feet high by 8 feet long by 4 feet deep is 1 cord. If a stack of wood contains 4 cords and is 4 feet high and 16 feet long, how deep must it be?**

  Ⓐ 16 feet

  Ⓑ 12 feet

  Ⓒ 8 feet

  Ⓓ 4 feet

Lesson 8-14   Name _____

1 **Which statement about this figure is false?**

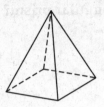

Ⓐ It has 5 corners (vertices).

Ⓑ It has 8 edges.

Ⓒ It has 6 faces.

Ⓓ It is a square pyramid.

2 **How many more edges are there in the cube than in the pyramid?**

Ⓕ 1

Ⓖ 2

Ⓗ 3

Ⓙ 4

3 **What is the number of triangular faces on a square pyramid?**

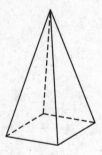

Ⓐ 3   Ⓒ 5

Ⓑ 4   Ⓓ 6

4 **Which statement about cylinders and cones is false?**

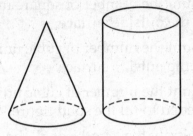

Ⓕ They can both roll.

Ⓖ They have at least one circular face each.

Ⓗ They are both solid figures.

Ⓙ They both have 2 edges.

5 **Which is a true statement about the faces of a rectangular prism?**

Ⓐ There are usually 3 pairs of rectangular faces.

Ⓑ There are always 6, all the same, square faces.

Ⓒ There might be 4 square faces and 4 rectangular faces.

Ⓓ There are usually 6, all the same, rectangular faces.

6 **If you break a sphere in half, the face created will be a —**

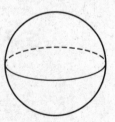

Ⓕ Triangle   Ⓗ Square

Ⓖ Circle   Ⓙ Rectangle

Lesson 8-15   Name _____

1 A group sets up the 2 tables below for a book sale. What is the surface area available for displaying books?

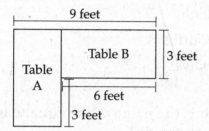

Ⓐ 36 square feet

Ⓑ 30 square feet

Ⓒ 27 square feet

Ⓓ 24 square feet

2 Mike stacked boxes for a grocery store display. He put 8 boxes side by side to make the bottom row. For the next row and each row after that, he used one less box than the row below it. The last row had one box. How many boxes did Mike use in his display?

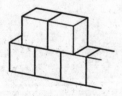

Ⓕ 40 boxes   Ⓗ 35 boxes

Ⓖ 36 boxes   Ⓙ 28 boxes

3 A breakfast cereal company used a box with a volume of 18 cubic units as shown. What was the total area of the surface of the box available for lettering?

Ⓐ 21 square units

Ⓑ 30 square units

Ⓒ 42 square units

Ⓓ 48 square units

4 A building in Richmond has a base of 50 meters by 20 meters and is 4 stories tall. Each story is about 3 meters. What is the volume of the building?

Ⓕ 3,000 cubic meters

Ⓖ 4,000 cubic meters

Ⓗ 12,000 cubic meters

Ⓙ 20,000 cubic meters

5 How are the two shaded garden plots alike? How are they different? Which garden plot would require the least fencing to enclose it? Use complete sentences in your answer.

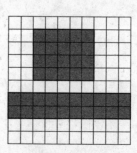

111

Lesson 9-1   Name _____

1 How many equal parts are there when you divide a figure into thirds?

Ⓐ 13 parts

Ⓑ 9 parts

Ⓒ 6 parts

Ⓓ 3 parts

2 Which is the name of the equal parts of the circle?

Ⓕ Fourths

Ⓖ Fifths

Ⓗ Sixths

Ⓙ Eighths

3 The teacher brought a dozen (12) apples to share with the class. She cut each apple in half. How many halves did she have?

Ⓐ 48 halves

Ⓑ 24 halves

Ⓒ 20 halves

Ⓓ 12 halves

4 Which is the name of 2 equal parts of a whole?

Ⓕ Eighths

Ⓖ Sixths

Ⓗ Fourths

Ⓙ Halves

5 Which is the name of the equal parts of the rectangle?

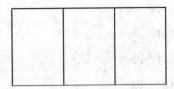

Ⓐ Halves

Ⓑ Thirds

Ⓒ Fourths

Ⓓ Fifths

6 Which is the name for the equal parts of the square?

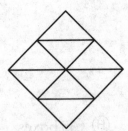

Ⓕ Fourths

Ⓖ Sixths

Ⓗ Eighths

Ⓙ Tenths

112

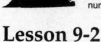

Lesson 9-2   Name _____

1 Which statement about fractions is false?

Ⓐ The denominator tells how many equal parts are in the whole.

Ⓑ The numerator tells how many of those parts are being described.

Ⓒ A fraction is a way of representing part of a whole or part of a group.

Ⓓ Fractions cannot be added or subtracted.

2 An apple pie was divided into 4 equal pieces. You ate 1 piece. What fraction of the apple pie did you eat?

Ⓕ $\frac{3}{4}$

Ⓖ $\frac{2}{4}$

Ⓗ $\frac{1}{3}$

Ⓙ $\frac{1}{4}$

3 Which picture shows $\frac{5}{8}$ of a pie left?

4 What fraction of the figure is shaded?

Ⓕ $\frac{1}{4}$

Ⓖ $\frac{1}{3}$

Ⓗ $\frac{4}{10}$

Ⓙ $\frac{1}{2}$

5 Which of these figures has $\frac{1}{4}$ shaded?

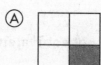

113

Lesson 9-3

Name _____

1 Which completes the pattern?

$$\frac{1}{2} = \frac{2}{4} = \frac{3}{6} = \frac{4}{8} = \frac{5}{10} = \frac{6}{\square}$$

- Ⓐ 11
- Ⓑ 12
- Ⓒ 13
- Ⓓ 14

2 Which fraction is equivalent to $\frac{2}{5}$?

- Ⓕ $\frac{2}{10}$
- Ⓖ $\frac{4}{10}$
- Ⓗ $\frac{5}{10}$
- Ⓙ $\frac{3}{6}$

3 Which fractions are not equivalent?

- Ⓐ $\frac{2}{3}$ and $\frac{3}{6}$
- Ⓑ $\frac{1}{3}$ and $\frac{2}{6}$
- Ⓒ $\frac{2}{8}$ and $\frac{3}{12}$
- Ⓓ $\frac{6}{10}$ and $\frac{3}{5}$

4 Which number completes the number sentence?

$$\frac{1}{5} = \frac{\square}{35}$$

- Ⓕ 5
- Ⓖ 6
- Ⓗ 7
- Ⓙ 8

5 Use the fraction strips in the figure to find the missing number?

$$\frac{2}{3} = \frac{\square}{6}$$

1		
$\frac{1}{3}$	$\frac{1}{3}$	
$\frac{1}{6}$ $\frac{1}{6}$	$\frac{1}{6}$ $\frac{1}{6}$	

- Ⓐ 2
- Ⓑ 3
- Ⓒ 4
- Ⓓ 5

6 Kenny finished $\frac{4}{6}$ of the math problems and Josh finished $\frac{6}{9}$ of the same problems. Did they finish the same fraction of the problems? _____

Explain your answer.

Lesson 9-4   Name _____

1 Order the fraction strips from least to greatest.

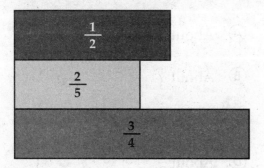

$\frac{1}{2}$

$\frac{2}{5}$

$\frac{3}{4}$

Ⓐ $\frac{3}{4}, \frac{1}{2}, \frac{2}{5}$

Ⓑ $\frac{2}{5}, \frac{3}{4}, \frac{1}{2}$

Ⓒ $\frac{2}{5}, \frac{1}{2}, \frac{3}{4}$

Ⓓ $\frac{1}{2}, \frac{2}{5}, \frac{3}{4}$

2 Hadensville is about halfway between Charlottesville and Richmond; Ferncliff is about $\frac{1}{4}$ of the way; and Gum Spring is about $\frac{2}{3}$ of the way. Which is the correct order of fractions from least to greatest, representing towns arranged nearest to farthest from Charlottesville?

Ⓕ $\frac{1}{2}, \frac{2}{3}, \frac{1}{4}$

Ⓖ $\frac{1}{2}, \frac{1}{4}, \frac{2}{3}$

Ⓗ $\frac{2}{3}, \frac{1}{2}, \frac{1}{4}$

Ⓙ $\frac{1}{4}, \frac{1}{2}, \frac{2}{3}$

3 Which shows the fractions ordered from greatest to least?

Ⓐ $\frac{7}{8}, \frac{1}{3}, \frac{3}{5}$

Ⓑ $\frac{7}{8}, \frac{3}{5}, \frac{1}{3}$

Ⓒ $\frac{1}{3}, \frac{3}{5}, \frac{7}{8}$

Ⓓ $\frac{1}{3}, \frac{7}{8}, \frac{3}{5}$

4 Which expression is false?

Ⓕ $\frac{1}{2} > \frac{1}{3}$

Ⓖ $\frac{6}{8} = \frac{9}{12}$

Ⓗ $\frac{1}{8} < \frac{1}{5}$

Ⓙ $\frac{1}{10} > \frac{1}{3}$

5 Which group of fractions is ordered from least to greatest?

Ⓐ $\frac{3}{4}, \frac{1}{2}, \frac{1}{8}$

Ⓑ $\frac{2}{3}, \frac{4}{6}, \frac{6}{9}$

Ⓒ $\frac{9}{10}, \frac{4}{8}, \frac{1}{4}$

Ⓓ $\frac{1}{5}, \frac{1}{3}, \frac{1}{2}$

Lesson 9-5   Name _____

1   **Estimate the amount that is shaded.**

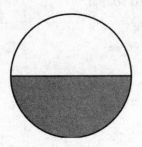

Ⓐ   About $\frac{1}{4}$

Ⓑ   About $\frac{1}{3}$

Ⓒ   About $\frac{1}{2}$

Ⓓ   About $\frac{2}{3}$

2   **Ms. Tibert's class baked a very big cookie. Part of the cookie was eaten during recess. Estimate the fraction of the cookie that was eaten.**

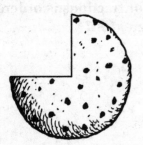

Ⓕ $\frac{1}{2}$ Ⓗ $\frac{1}{4}$

Ⓖ $\frac{1}{3}$ Ⓙ $\frac{1}{5}$

3   **Tom has \$11. He gives \$3 to Jim and \$2 to Kenny. About what fraction of his money does Tom have left?**

Ⓐ   About $\frac{1}{4}$

Ⓑ   About $\frac{1}{3}$

Ⓒ   About $\frac{1}{2}$

Ⓓ   About $\frac{2}{3}$

4   **Which is the BEST estimate for how much of the circle is shaded?**

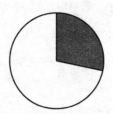

Ⓕ   About $\frac{1}{3}$

Ⓖ   About $\frac{1}{8}$

Ⓗ   About $\frac{2}{3}$

Ⓙ   About $\frac{3}{4}$

5   **Draw a circle and shade about $\frac{3}{5}$ of it. Write the fraction for the unshaded part.**

SOL 3.5b The student will name and write the fraction represented by a given model (... length/measurement ...). Fractions (including mixed numbers) will include halves, thirds, fourths, eighths and tenths.

Lesson 9-6   Name _____

1 Which fraction is represented by the dot on the number line?

- Ⓐ $\frac{4}{10}$
- Ⓑ $\frac{4}{8}$
- Ⓒ $\frac{6}{10}$
- Ⓓ $\frac{5}{8}$

2 Which fractions would be in order from left to right on the number line?

- Ⓕ $\frac{6}{10}, \frac{3}{10}, \frac{9}{10}$
- Ⓖ $\frac{3}{10}, \frac{9}{10}, \frac{6}{10}$
- Ⓗ $\frac{3}{10}, \frac{6}{10}, \frac{9}{10}$
- Ⓙ $\frac{9}{10}, \frac{6}{10}, \frac{3}{10}$

3 Which fraction is represented by the dot on the number line?

- Ⓐ $\frac{2}{6}$
- Ⓑ $\frac{4}{8}$
- Ⓒ $\frac{5}{8}$
- Ⓓ $\frac{4}{6}$

4 Which fraction is between $\frac{2}{4}$ and $\frac{3}{4}$?

- Ⓕ $\frac{1}{4}$
- Ⓖ $\frac{4}{8}$
- Ⓗ $\frac{5}{8}$
- Ⓙ $\frac{6}{8}$

5 Ann and Maggie live one mile apart. If the soccer field is between their houses and is $\frac{5}{8}$ of a mile from Maggie's house, how far is it from Ann's house? Use the number line below. Show the approximate location of the soccer field. Explain your answer.

Ann's House   Maggie's House

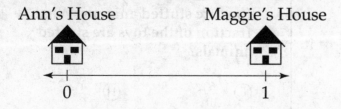

SOL 3.5a The student will divide … sets to represent a fraction.
SOL 3.5b The student will name and write the fraction represented by a given model (… set). Fractions (including mixed numbers) will include halves, thirds, fourths, eighths and tenths.

Lesson 9-7   Name _____

1 Four boys and six girls went on a field trip to the Science Museum of Virginia. What fraction of the students are boys?

(A) $\frac{4}{10}$

(B) $\frac{5}{10}$

(C) $\frac{6}{10}$

(D) $\frac{4}{6}$

2 Josh did 6 out of 8 of his math homework problems. What fraction of the problems did he still have to do?

(F) $\frac{6}{8}$

(G) $\frac{6}{14}$

(H) $\frac{2}{6}$

(J) $\frac{2}{8}$

3 What fraction of the circles is shaded?

(A) $\frac{1}{4}$

(B) $\frac{1}{3}$

(C) $\frac{2}{4}$

(D) $\frac{3}{4}$

4 There are 5 cars and 5 buses parked near the Virginia Capitol building. What fraction of the vehicles are buses?

(F) $\frac{2}{5}$

(G) $\frac{5}{10}$

(H) $\frac{6}{10}$

(J) $\frac{5}{5}$

5 Triangles can fit together to make a hexagon. What fraction of the hexagon is one triangle?

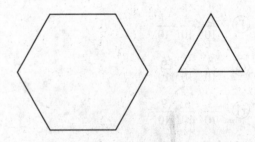

(A) $\frac{1}{8}$

(B) $\frac{1}{6}$

(C) $\frac{1}{5}$

(D) $\frac{1}{4}$

6 Yolanda has 10 toys. Six are dolls and four are stuffed animals. What fraction of the toys are stuffed animals?

(F) $\frac{6}{10}$ (H) $\frac{4}{6}$

(G) $\frac{5}{10}$ (J) $\frac{4}{10}$

Lesson 9-8   Name _____

1   Which is $\frac{1}{2}$ of the 12 cars?

    Ⓐ 8

    Ⓑ 6

    Ⓒ 4

    Ⓓ 2

2   What is $\frac{1}{8}$ of 48?

    Ⓕ 6

    Ⓖ 7

    Ⓗ 8

    Ⓙ 9

3   There are 100 centimeters in a meter. Justin used $\frac{1}{10}$ of a meter of string for a craft he was making. How many centimeters of string did he use?

    Ⓐ 1,000

    Ⓑ 100

    Ⓒ 10

    Ⓓ 1

4   What is $\frac{1}{3}$ of 9 peanuts?

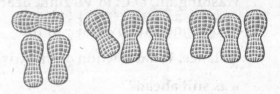

    Ⓕ 2 peanuts

    Ⓖ 3 peanuts

    Ⓗ 4 peanuts

    Ⓙ 6 peanuts

5   A farmer living near Lynchburg planted vegetables in $\frac{1}{8}$ of his 200 acre farm. How many acres of vegetables did he plant?

    Ⓐ 20

    Ⓑ 25

    Ⓒ 30

    Ⓓ 40

6   One day, during a march to Washington D.C., walkers covered $\frac{1}{4}$ of the 120 miles they planned to walk. How far did they walk that day?

    Ⓕ 10 miles

    Ⓖ 20 miles

    Ⓗ 25 miles

    Ⓙ 30 miles

SOL 3.11 The student will add and subtract with proper fractions having like denominators of 10 or less, using ... pictorial models representing areas/regions....

Lesson 9-9   Name _____

1 Michael was driving from Washington, D.C. to Virginia Beach. In one hour he covered $\frac{1}{4}$ of the distance. What fraction of the drive was still ahead?

Ⓐ $\frac{1}{4}$ Ⓒ $\frac{3}{4}$

Ⓑ $\frac{1}{2}$ Ⓓ $\frac{5}{8}$

2 Tom ate $\frac{2}{8}$ of an apple pie. His sister Sue ate $\frac{1}{8}$ of the pie. What fraction of the pie was left for the rest of the family?

Ⓕ $\frac{3}{8}$ Ⓗ $\frac{5}{8}$

Ⓖ $\frac{4}{8}$ Ⓙ $\frac{6}{8}$

3 Use the model below to solve the equation.

$$\frac{6}{8} - \frac{3}{8} = \square$$

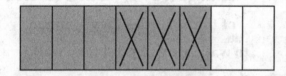

Ⓐ $\frac{4}{8}$ Ⓒ $\frac{2}{8}$

Ⓑ $\frac{3}{8}$ Ⓓ $\frac{1}{8}$

4 Which is the fraction that makes the sentence true?

$$\frac{1}{3} + \square = \frac{3}{3}$$

Ⓕ $\frac{1}{3}$ Ⓗ $\frac{3}{3}$

Ⓖ $\frac{2}{3}$ Ⓙ $\frac{4}{3}$

5 Use the model below to solve the equation.

$$\frac{7}{10} - \frac{3}{10} = \square$$

Ⓐ $\frac{10}{10}$ Ⓒ $\frac{5}{10}$

Ⓑ $\frac{7}{10}$ Ⓓ $\frac{4}{10}$

6 What is $\frac{3}{4} - \frac{1}{4} = \square$?

Ⓕ $\frac{2}{0}$

Ⓖ $\frac{4}{4}$

Ⓗ $\frac{2}{4}$

Ⓙ $\frac{1}{4}$

Lesson 9-10   Name _____

1 Louis and Marsha were hiking the Appalachian trail in Virginia. On a Sunday they hiked for $2\frac{1}{2}$ hours before stopping for lunch in Troutville. How long did they hike that morning?

Ⓐ 90 minutes

Ⓑ 100 minutes

Ⓒ 125 minutes

Ⓓ 150 minutes

2 How many circles are in the picture?

Ⓕ 3   Ⓗ $3\frac{1}{2}$

Ⓖ $3\frac{1}{3}$ Ⓙ $3\frac{2}{3}$

3 Hannah made 20 cookies. She ate 2 and gave the rest in equal amounts to her 4 friends. Exactly how many did each friend get?

Ⓐ 5 cookies

Ⓑ $4\frac{1}{2}$ cookies

Ⓒ $4\frac{1}{4}$ cookies

Ⓓ 4 cookies

4 A farmer has 18 acres of land that he wants to divide among his 8 grown children. Use the model below to calculate the exact amount of land that each person will get.

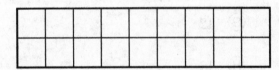

Ⓕ 2 acres   Ⓗ $2\frac{1}{4}$ acres

Ⓖ $2\frac{1}{8}$ acres   Ⓙ $2\frac{1}{2}$ acres

5 Miriam made 5 sandwiches to share equally with Jessica, Chloe, and Jenny. How did the 4 girls share the sandwiches? Draw one girl's share and label it with a mixed number. Explain your answer.

Lesson 9-11   Name _____

1 Ashley and her family are driving to Florida for winter vacation. On the first morning they drove for $3\frac{1}{4}$ hours at 60 miles per hour. How far did they drive?

Ⓐ 180 miles

Ⓑ 190 miles

Ⓒ 195 miles

Ⓓ 200 miles

2 Three friends are sharing 4 chocolate bars. Each chocolate bar has 12 pieces. How many pieces did each person get?

Ⓕ $1\frac{1}{3}$

Ⓖ 12

Ⓗ 15

Ⓙ 16

3 A teacher is trying to decide how to seat 3 students, Andy, Claire and Drew, in a row. How many ways are possible?

Ⓐ 2 ways

Ⓑ 3 ways

Ⓒ 4 ways

Ⓓ 6 ways

4 The Confederation Bridge linking Prince Edward Island to mainland Canada took 42 months to build. How many years is that?

Ⓕ 4 years

Ⓖ $3\frac{1}{2}$ years

Ⓗ $3\frac{1}{3}$ years

Ⓙ 3 years

5 Hikers on the Appalachian trail walk at 3 miles per hour. How far will they hike in 100 minutes?

Ⓐ 4 miles

Ⓑ 5 miles

Ⓒ 6 miles

Ⓓ 300 miles

6 There are 640 acres in a square mile. This is called 1 section. How many acres in a $\frac{1}{4}$ section?

Ⓕ 100 acres

Ⓖ 160 acres

Ⓗ 320 acres

Ⓙ 480 acres

Lesson 9-12   Name _____

1   Which statement about measuring length is false?

   Ⓐ The inch is the customary unit of measure used in the United States.

   Ⓑ The meter is the standard unit of measure used by the rest of the world.

   Ⓒ Perimeter is the distance around a figure.

   Ⓓ There are 10 inches in 1 foot.

2   Estimate and then measure the length of the crayon to the nearest inch.

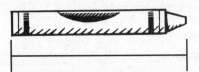

   Ⓕ 1 inch

   Ⓖ 2 inches

   Ⓗ 3 inches

   Ⓙ 4 inches

3   Estimate and then measure the perimeter of this rectangle to the nearest inch.

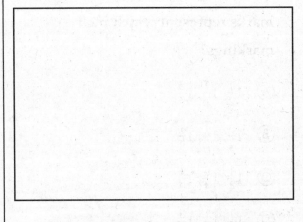

   Ⓐ 25 inches   Ⓒ 5 inches

   Ⓑ 10 inches   Ⓓ 3 inches

4   Estimate and then measure the height of the soup can to the nearest inch.

   Ⓕ 1 inch   Ⓗ 3 inches

   Ⓖ 2 inches   Ⓙ 4 inches

5   Draw a right triangle that has a base of 3 inches and is 2 inches high. Explain how to draw the triangle.

Lesson 9-13   Name _____

1 A ruler has a tick mark every $\frac{1}{4}$ inch. From smallest to largest, the tick marks between the 1-inch and 2-inch marks represent which inch markings?

Ⓐ $1\frac{1}{2}, 1\frac{1}{4}, 1\frac{3}{4}$

Ⓑ $1\frac{3}{4}, 1\frac{1}{2}, 1\frac{1}{4}$

Ⓒ $1\frac{1}{4}, 1\frac{3}{4}, 1\frac{1}{2}$

Ⓓ $1\frac{1}{4}, 1\frac{1}{2}, 1\frac{3}{4}$

2 Measure the pencil to the CLOSEST $\frac{1}{2}$ inch.

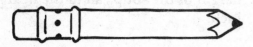

Ⓕ $1\frac{1}{2}$ in.

Ⓖ 2 in.

Ⓗ $2\frac{1}{2}$ in.

Ⓙ 3 in.

3 Which cannot be a length measured to the CLOSEST $\frac{1}{2}$ inch?

Ⓐ 2 in.   Ⓒ $2\frac{1}{2}$ in.

Ⓑ $2\frac{1}{4}$ in.   Ⓓ $3\frac{1}{2}$ in.

4 Measure the pencil to the CLOSEST $\frac{1}{4}$ inch.

Ⓕ 2 in.   Ⓗ $2\frac{1}{2}$ in.

Ⓖ $2\frac{1}{4}$ in.   Ⓙ $2\frac{3}{4}$ in.

5 Measure the crayon to the CLOSEST $\frac{1}{4}$ inch.

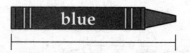

Ⓐ $1\frac{1}{2}$ in.   Ⓒ $2\frac{1}{4}$ in.

Ⓑ $1\frac{3}{4}$ in.   Ⓓ $2\frac{3}{4}$ in.

6 Which point is incorrectly labeled on the number line below?

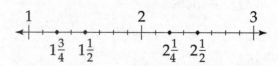

Ⓕ $1\frac{3}{4}$ in.   Ⓗ $2\frac{1}{4}$ in.

Ⓖ $1\frac{1}{2}$ in.   Ⓙ $2\frac{1}{2}$ in.

Lesson 9-14   Name _____

1 **Which is 5 feet, 5 inches in inches?**

Ⓐ 55 in.

Ⓑ 60 in.

Ⓒ 65 in.

Ⓓ 70 in.

2 **Which is $2\frac{1}{2}$ feet in inches?**

Ⓕ 30 in.

Ⓖ 28 in.

Ⓗ 26 in.

Ⓙ 24 in.

3 **The lifeguard stations at Virginia Beach are about $6\frac{1}{4}$ feet high. How high are they in inches?**

Ⓐ 72 in.

Ⓑ 75 in.

Ⓒ 76 in.

Ⓓ 78 in.

4 **Which is 40 inches in feet and inches?**

Ⓕ 3 ft, 2 in.

Ⓖ 3 ft, 3 in.

Ⓗ 3 ft, 4 in.

Ⓙ 3 ft, 6 in.

5 **Which is 18 inches in feet?**

Ⓐ $1\frac{1}{4}$ ft

Ⓑ $1\frac{1}{2}$ ft

Ⓒ $1\frac{3}{4}$ in.

Ⓓ 2 ft

6 **Eric is 4 feet, 8 inches tall. How tall is he in feet?**

Ⓕ $4\frac{4}{8}$ ft

Ⓖ $4\frac{5}{8}$ ft

Ⓗ $4\frac{2}{3}$ ft

Ⓙ $4\frac{7}{8}$ ft

7 **Estimate your height in feet and inches.** _____
Rewrite your height in inches. _____
Show your calculations.

With a ruler, measure your height in inches and compare your answer. _____

Lesson 9-15   Name _____

1 How many feet are in 10 yards?

(A) 12 ft   (C) 30 ft

(B) 24 ft   (D) 36 ft

2 How many yards tall is a man whose height is 72 inches?

(F) 6 yd   (H) 2 yd

(G) 4 yd   (J) 1 yd

3 Which measurement is MOST LIKELY to be the height of a house?

(A) 35 in.   (C) 35 yd

(B) 35 ft   (D) 35 mi

4 Jim ran 6 laps around the track. One lap is 1,320 feet or $\frac{1}{4}$ of a mile. Which is the total distance he ran in feet and miles?

(F) 2,640 ft; $\frac{1}{2}$ mi

(G) 5,280 ft; 1 mi

(H) 7,920 ft; $1\frac{1}{2}$ mi

(J) 10,560 ft; 2 mi

5 Which number sentence is not true?

(A) 3 yd = 108 in.

(B) 1 mi > 2,000 yd

(C) 6 yd < 20 ft

(D) 65 in. > 5 ft

6 Which number sentence is true?

(F) 2 yd > 90 in.

(G) 1 mi < 5,000 ft

(H) 6 yd = 216 in.

(J) 3 ft = 24 in.

7 How many feet are in 3 miles?

(A) 5,280

(B) 10,560

(C) 15,840

(D) 63,360

8 How many yards are in 3 miles?

(F) 63,360

(G) 15,840

(H) 10,560

(J) 5,280

9 Luke is paid $8 for every foot of fence he installs. How much will he be paid for putting up 200 yards of fence? Show your work.

_____

Lesson 9-16   Name _____

1 **Which statement about bar graphs is not true?**

Ⓐ Bar graphs visually represent data.

Ⓑ Each bar shows one category.

Ⓒ The counts for the categories are represented by the lengths of the bars.

Ⓓ There must be at least four categories shown on a bar graph.

2 **Clara collected seashells near Virginia Beach and found 5 sand dollars. She made a graph but forgot to put the number of shells on the graph. How many clam shells and periwinkle shells did she find?**

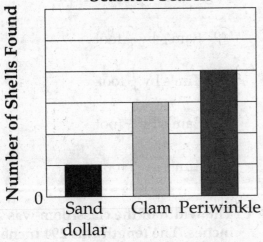

Horseneck Beach Seashell Search

Number of Shells Found

Type of Seashells

Ⓕ Not enough information

Ⓖ 10, 15

Ⓗ 12, 16

Ⓙ 15, 20

A 4-H club vote on favorite farm animals gave the results below. Each member of the club got one vote. The animals that got the most votes are shown on the graph.

Use the graph for 1–3.

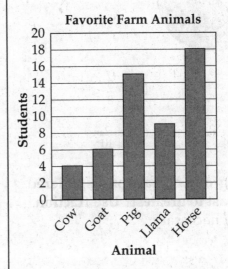

Favorite Farm Animals

Students

Cow Goat Pig Llama Horse

Animal

3 **How many members are in the 4-H club?**

Ⓐ 5

Ⓑ Less than 51

Ⓒ 51

Ⓓ More than 51

4 **How many more club members chose horse than chose llama?**

Ⓕ 7   Ⓗ 9

Ⓖ 8   Ⓙ 10

5 **How many club members voted for chicken?**

Ⓐ 4   Ⓒ 0

Ⓑ 2   Ⓓ Not enough information

127

Lesson 9-17   Name _____

1 **What fraction of the pie was eaten?**

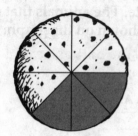

(A) $\frac{3}{5}$ (C) $\frac{3}{8}$

(B) $\frac{3}{7}$ (D) $\frac{3}{10}$

2 **Which group of fractions is ordered from least to greatest? Use fraction strips if necessary.**

(F) $\frac{1}{2}, \frac{3}{10}, \frac{5}{8}, \frac{2}{3}$

(G) $\frac{2}{3}, \frac{5}{8}, \frac{1}{2}, \frac{3}{10}$

(H) $\frac{3}{10}, \frac{1}{2}, \frac{2}{3}, \frac{5}{8}$

(J) $\frac{3}{10}, \frac{1}{2}, \frac{5}{8}, \frac{2}{3}$

3 **What fraction of the vegetables are tomatoes?**

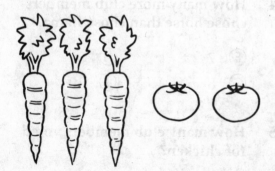

(A) $\frac{2}{3}$ (C) $\frac{2}{5}$

(B) $\frac{3}{5}$ (D) $\frac{1}{3}$

4 **Farmer Clem was planting 80 acres of corn. By noon, he had 32 acres planted. What fraction of the 80 acres did he still have to plant?**

(F) $\frac{4}{10}$

(G) $\frac{6}{10}$

(H) $\frac{2}{3}$

(J) $\frac{8}{10}$

5 **Tim and Sam each measured the length of the classroom. Tim measured $24\frac{1}{2}$ feet. Sam measured $24\frac{5}{8}$ feet. Which measurement is larger and by how much?**

(A) Sam's by $\frac{3}{8}$ foot

(B) Tim's by $\frac{1}{8}$ foot

(C) Sam's by $\frac{1}{8}$ foot

(D) Tim's by $\frac{3}{8}$ foot

6 **The width of the classroom was 216 inches. The length was 294 inches. How much longer was the length?**

(F) 72 inches

(G) 75 inches

(H) 78 inches

(J) 510 inches

Lesson 10-1   Name _____

1   What number is represented by the shaded part of the figure below?

Ⓐ   0.03

Ⓑ   0.3

Ⓒ   3

Ⓓ   30

2   Susan cut a pear into 10 equal pieces. She ate 6 pieces. Which decimal shows how much of the pear she ate?

Ⓕ   0.06   Ⓗ   6

Ⓖ   0.6   Ⓙ   6.10

3   This is a whole.

What is   **?**

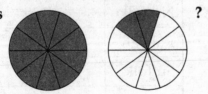

Ⓐ   1.02   Ⓒ   12

Ⓑ   1.2   Ⓓ   120

4   Out of 10 friends who went horseback riding in the Cumberland State Forest, 4 rode white horses and the rest rode brown horses. Which decimal shows the part of the group of friends who rode brown horses?

Ⓕ   0.2

Ⓖ   0.4

Ⓗ   0.6

Ⓙ   0.8

5   Which shows four tenths?

Ⓐ   0.004

Ⓑ   0.04

Ⓒ   0.4

Ⓓ   4

6   A hiking trail in the Blue Ridge Mountains is $3\frac{8}{10}$ miles long. Which shows that distance written as a decimal?

Ⓕ   38

Ⓖ   3.8

Ⓗ   0.38

Ⓙ   0.038

7   Carlos says that 2.5 is the same as two wholes and 25 tenths. Do you agree with him? Explain why you do or do not agree.

Lesson 10-2   Name _____

1   What number is represented by the shaded part of the figure below?

- (A) 0.37
- (B) 0.037
- (C) 0.63
- (D) 0.063

2   The chart shows the number of CDs of each type that Robert owns.

Type of CD	Number of CDs
Rock	25
Classical	32
Jazz	23
Country	20

Which decimal shows the part of his CD collection that is jazz?

- (F) 23
- (G) 2.3
- (H) 0.23
- (J) 0.023

3   What is $2\frac{50}{100}$ written as a decimal?

- (A) 2.75
- (B) 2.50
- (C) 2.25
- (D) 2.00

4   What number is represented by the shaded part of the figure below?

- (F) 1.17
- (H) 0.017
- (G) 1.017
- (J) 0.17

5   Shanna's mother is 48 years old. Which decimal shows the part of a century (a century is 100 years) that Shanna's mother has been alive?

- (A) 48
- (B) 4.8
- (C) 0.48
- (D) 0.048

6   The table shows yearly rainfall amounts for some Virginia cities.

City	Rainfall (inches)
Norfolk	7.35
Raleigh	7.58
Suffolk	7.28
Emporia	7.45

For which city is the number in the tenths place a 5?

- (F) Norfolk
- (G) Raleigh
- (H) Suffolk
- (J) Emporia

130

Lesson 10-3   Name _____

1 Which group of decimals is in order from greatest to least?

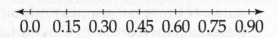

0.0 0.15 0.30 0.45 0.60 0.75 0.90

- (A) 0.90, 0.42, 0.07
- (B) 0.45, 0.46, 0.06
- (C) 0.63, 0.35, 0.42
- (D) 0.24, 0.35, 0.79

2 Which number makes the number sentence true?

$$0.57 < \boxed{}$$

- (F) 0.42
- (H) 0.057
- (G) 0.57
- (J) 0.61

3 The heights of four cats are shown below.

Height of Cat

Feet	0.78	0.67	0.74	0.83

How tall is the shortest cat that was measured?

- (A) 0.78 ft
- (C) 0.74 ft
- (B) 0.67 ft
- (D) 0.83 ft

4 On a number line, which of the following would come between 1.25 and 2.39?

- (F) 1.04
- (H) 2.48
- (G) 1.29
- (J) 2.57

5 Which is the greatest number?

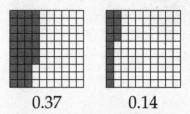

0.37   0.14

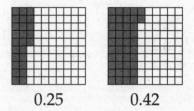

0.25   0.42

- (A) 0.25
- (C) 0.42
- (B) 0.37
- (D) 0.14

6 The table shows the lengths of some colored ribbons.

Color	Length (ft)
Red	1.19
Blue	0.9
Green	0.95
Yellow	0.65

Which two ribbons were CLOSEST in length?

- (F) Red and yellow
- (G) Blue and green
- (H) Red and green
- (J) Blue and yellow

Lesson 10-4   Name _____

1
$$\begin{array}{r} 5.0 \\ -\ 1.3 \\ \hline \end{array}$$

   Ⓐ 3.7

   Ⓑ 4.3

   Ⓒ 4.7

   Ⓓ 6.3

2
$$\begin{array}{r} 4.7 \\ 3.2 \\ +\ 5.1 \\ \hline \end{array}$$

   Ⓕ 12.0

   Ⓖ 12.9

   Ⓗ 13.0

   Ⓙ 13.9

3 $5.6 + 10.5 =$

   Ⓐ 16.1

   Ⓑ 15.1

   Ⓒ 4.9

   Ⓓ 3.9

4 $5.0 - 3.9 =$

   Ⓕ 1.1

   Ⓖ 1.9

   Ⓗ 2.0

   Ⓙ 8.9

5 The distance around the Philpott Reservoir is 15.4 miles, and the distance around Claytor Lake is 7.6 miles. If Chris ran around Philpott Reservoir, then drove to Claytor Lake and ran around the lake, what is the total distance that he ran?

   Ⓐ 2.3 miles

   Ⓑ 22.0 miles

   Ⓒ 23.0 miles

   Ⓓ 23.1 miles

6 It is 2.7 miles from Sarah's house to school. It is 1.8 miles from Sarah's house to Beth's house. How much farther is it from Sarah's house to school, than from Sarah's house to Beth's house?

   Ⓕ 0.9 miles

   Ⓖ 1.9 miles

   Ⓗ 3.5 miles

   Ⓙ 4.5 miles

7 Which number makes the number sentence true?

$$0.3 = 0.2 + \boxed{}$$

   Ⓐ 1

   Ⓑ 1.0

   Ⓒ 0.1

   Ⓓ 0.01

Lesson 10-5   Name _____

1 The table below shows the different colors and kinds of shirts that the baseball team can choose from.

Color   Kind of Shirt

Blue — Jersey
       — T-shirt
       — Sweatshirt

White — Jersey
       — T-shirt
       — Sweatshirt

Which of the following lists all the different ways to combine colors and shirts?

Ⓐ Blue jersey
    Blue T-shirt
    Blue sweatshirt
    White jersey
    White T-shirt
    White sweatshirt

Ⓑ Blue T-shirt
    Blue jersey
    White jersey
    White jersey

Ⓒ Blue jersey
    Blue sweatshirt
    White T-shirt
    White jersey
    White sweatshirt

Ⓓ Blue T-shirt
    Blue sweatshirt
    White jersey
    White sweatshirt

2 Three coins are in a jar: a penny, a nickel, and a dime. In how many different orders can you take the coins out of the jar?

Ⓕ 1
Ⓖ 3
Ⓗ 4
Ⓙ 6

3 The dashed line in the figure is a diagonal.

How many diagonals does this square have?

Ⓐ 1   Ⓒ 3
Ⓑ 2   Ⓓ 4

4 You can have two kinds of bread, white or wheat, and two kinds of meat, ham or turkey. How many different kinds of sandwiches can you make?

Ⓕ 2   Ⓗ 6
Ⓖ 4   Ⓙ 8

5 Hilary is preparing for the first day of school. She makes a list of the three things she will ask her mother to buy: Tape, Ruler, Notebook. What are six different ways in which Hilary can list the items?

Lesson 10-6   Name _____

1 Use your centimeter ruler to help you answer this question.

Which is CLOSEST to the length of the pencil?

- Ⓐ 1 centimeter
- Ⓑ 3 centimeters
- Ⓒ 6 centimeters
- Ⓓ 9 centimeters

2 Use your centimeter ruler to help you answer this question.

Which is CLOSEST to the perimeter of the rectangle?

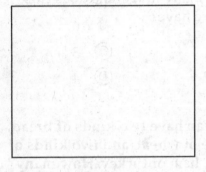

- Ⓕ 16 centimeters
- Ⓖ 18 centimeters
- Ⓗ 20 centimeters
- Ⓙ 22 centimeters

3 1 decimeter is equal to how many centimeters?

- Ⓐ 1
- Ⓒ 100
- Ⓑ 10
- Ⓓ 1000

4 Use your centimeter ruler to help you answer this question.

Which is CLOSEST to the length of the paper clip?

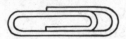

- Ⓕ 1 centimeters
- Ⓗ 4 centimeters
- Ⓖ 3 centimeters
- Ⓙ 5 centimeters

5 Use your centimeter ruler to help you answer this question.

Which is CLOSEST to the distance between the two basketballs?

- Ⓐ 3 centimeters
- Ⓒ 5 centimeters
- Ⓑ 4 centimeters
- Ⓓ 6 centimeters

6 Use your centimeter ruler to help you answer this question.

Which is CLOSEST to the length of the caterpillar?

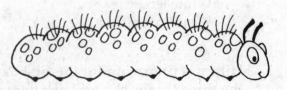

- Ⓕ 1 centimeter
- Ⓗ 5 centimeters
- Ⓖ 3 centimeters
- Ⓙ 7 centimeters

134

Lesson 10-7   Name _____

1   Which of the following is the best estimate of the length of a hiking trail through the Appalachian Mountains?

Ⓐ 5 kilometers   Ⓒ 5 decimeters

Ⓑ 5 meters   Ⓓ 5 centimeters

2   The chart shows the distances, in kilometers, between several cities in Virginia.

To	From	Distance (km)
Richmond	Norfolk	120
Norfolk	Petersburg	100
Petersburg	Charlottesville	135
Charlottesville	Waynesboro	40

How much farther is it between Petersburg and Charlottesville, than between Charlottesville and Waynesboro?

Ⓕ 20 kilometers

Ⓖ 35 kilometers

Ⓗ 80 kilometers

Ⓙ 95 kilometers

3   Which of the following would you measure in centimeters?

Ⓐ The distance to the moon

Ⓑ The length of your bedroom

Ⓒ The distance to a friend's house

Ⓓ The width of your hand

4   Which unit of measurement would you use to describe the length of your classroom?

Ⓕ Centimeters

Ⓖ Decimeters

Ⓗ Meters

Ⓙ Kilometers

5   The ceiling in Vinnie's bedroom is 5 meters high. What is its height in centimeters?

Ⓐ 50

Ⓑ 500

Ⓒ 5,000

Ⓓ 50,000

6   Which pair of numbers makes the sentence true?

4 meters = ☐ centimeters

= ☐ decimeters

Ⓕ 4, 40

Ⓖ 40, 4

Ⓗ 400, 40

Ⓙ 40, 400

7   Would you measure the length of your math book in —

Ⓐ centimeters

Ⓑ meters

Ⓒ kilometers

Ⓓ grams

Lesson 10-8   Name _____

1 Heidi prepared for a 5-kilometer race by running every day. The distances she ran are in the table below.

Day	Distance of Run
1	1 kilometer
2	1.5 kilometers
3	2.0 kilometers
4	2.5 kilometers

If this pattern continues, how far would Heidi run on day 6?

Ⓐ 3.0 kilometers

Ⓑ 3.5 kilometers

Ⓒ 4.0 kilometers

Ⓓ 4.5 kilometers

2 Roman bought 5 packs of pens. Each pack contained 8 pens. How many pens did Roman buy?

Ⓕ 12   Ⓗ 40

Ⓖ 20   Ⓙ 45

3   64 ÷ 8 =

Ⓐ 4

Ⓑ 8

Ⓒ 16

Ⓓ 32

4 Look at the pattern of shapes below.

If the pattern continues in the same way, what will be the next shape?

Ⓕ △   Ⓗ ▮

Ⓖ ⊙   Ⓙ ●

5 The table below shows the number of life jackets for the kayaking team.

Number of Kayaks	2	4	6	8	10
Number of Life Jackets	6	12	18	24	?

If the pattern in the table continues, how many life jackets are needed for 10 kayaks?

Ⓐ 24   Ⓒ 28

Ⓑ 26   Ⓓ 30

6 In Richmond, a snowstorm lasted four days. The amount of snow on the ground was 10 centimeters.

Stuart claims this is 1 meter of snow. Is he correct? Explain.

Lesson 10-9   Name _____

Use the graph for 1–2.

1 The picture graph below shows the number of inches of snow that fell in each of four months in Charlottesville.

Number of Inches of Snow

December	❄❄
January	❄❄❄❄
February	❄❄❄
March	❄❄

Each ❄ = 3 inches of snow

How many inches of snow fell in Charlottesville in February?

Ⓐ 6 inches   Ⓒ 12 inches

Ⓑ 9 inches   Ⓓ 15 inches

2 How much snow in all fell in Charlottesville from December through March?

Ⓕ 11 in.   Ⓗ 30 in.

Ⓖ 22 in.   Ⓙ 33 in.

3 The population of Evergreen is 4,036 and the population of Dixie is 2,984. Which is the sum of the populations of the two towns?

Ⓐ 2,021   Ⓒ 6,089

Ⓑ 5,683   Ⓓ 7,020

Dan kept track of the number of cups of lemonade he sold at his lemonade stand during one week. Use his bar graph for 4–5.

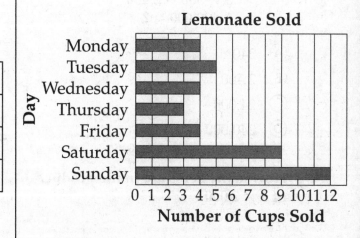

Lemonade Sold

4 How many more cups of lemonade did he sell on Sunday than on Tuesday?

Ⓕ 4   Ⓗ 6

Ⓖ 5   Ⓙ 7

5 What was the total number of cups of lemonade Dan sold that week?

Ⓐ 38   Ⓒ 40

Ⓑ 39   Ⓓ 41

6 Stacey learned that Mount Rogers is 5,729 feet tall and that Elliot Knob is 4,463 feet high. What is the sum of the elevations of the two mountain peaks?

Ⓕ 8,192 feet   Ⓗ 10,192 feet

Ⓖ 9,192 feet   Ⓙ 11,192 feet

Lesson 11-1   Name _____

1 **Which number completes the pattern?**

$3 \times 8 = 24$
$3 \times 80 = 240$
$3 \times 800 = 2,400$
$3 \times 8,000 = ?$

(A) 240

(B) 2,400

(C) 24,000

(D) 240,000

2 **How many zeros are in the product of 5 × 2,000?**

(F) 3

(G) 4

(H) 5

(J) 6

3 $3 \times 6,000 = \square$

(A) 1,800

(B) 3,600

(C) 18,000

(D) 36,000

4 **Which number makes the following equation true?**

$\square \times 5 = 400$

(F) 8

(G) 80

(H) 800

(J) 8,000

5 **Stanley measured his heart rate by checking his pulse. His heart beat 70 times in one minute. How many times would you expect his heart to beat in one hour?**

(A) 2,800

(B) 3,600

(C) 4,200

(D) 5,600

6 **At the school play, there are 20 rows of 30 seats set up. How many seats are available for the play?**

(F) 30

(G) 60

(H) 300

(J) 600

7 There are 50 nickels in a roll, and a roll of nickels is worth 250 cents. Stu is 4 nickels short of having 3 full rolls of nickels. Explain how you can figure out how much money Stu has. Then explain how you can figure out how many rolls of nickels are needed to make 10 dollars.

_____

_____

Lesson 11-2   Name _____

1 There are 466 paper clips in a jar. What is that number rounded to the nearest hundred?

Ⓐ 400

Ⓑ 460

Ⓒ 470

Ⓓ 500

2 Which is the BEST estimate for the product of 7 × 595?

Ⓕ 4,200

Ⓖ 4,800

Ⓗ 5,200

Ⓙ 5,600

3 What is the BEST estimate of 6 × 475?

Ⓐ 240

Ⓑ 300

Ⓒ 2,400

Ⓓ 3,000

4 What is the BEST estimate of 9 × 109?

Ⓕ 90

Ⓖ 180

Ⓗ 900

Ⓙ 1,800

5 What is the BEST estimate of 9 × 99?

Ⓐ 90   Ⓒ 900

Ⓑ 100   Ⓓ 1,000

6 What is the BEST estimate of 6 × 407?

Ⓕ 240

Ⓖ 2,000

Ⓗ 2,400

Ⓙ 3,000

7 There are 5,280 feet in 1 mile. Estimate the number of feet in 2 miles.

Ⓐ 1,000

Ⓑ 9,000

Ⓒ 10,000

Ⓓ 12,000

8 Kevin wants to estimate how many pieces his puzzle has. He counts 38 pieces in $\frac{1}{4}$ of the puzzle. Which of the following is the BEST estimate of the total number of pieces the puzzle has?

Ⓕ 10

Ⓖ 120

Ⓗ 160

Ⓙ 200

Lesson 11-3   Name _____

1 Which number completes the pattern?

$$40 \div 8 = 5$$
$$400 \div 8 = 50$$
$$4,000 \div 8 =$$

- (A) 50
- (B) 500
- (C) 5,000
- (D) 50,000

2 Which division fact will help you find $3,600 \div 9$?

- (F) $36 \div 4$
- (G) $36 \div 9$
- (H) $36 \div 6$
- (J) $36 \div 2$

3 How many zeros are in the quotient of $2,000 \div 4$?

- (A) 2
- (B) 3
- (C) 4
- (D) 5

4 Use mental math to find the quotient of $240 \div 3$.

- (F) 8
- (G) 40
- (H) 60
- (J) 80

5 1,600 divided by 8 is —

- (A) 16 hundreds $\div$ 8
- (B) $160 \div 8$
- (C) 16 hundreds $\div$ 80
- (D) 16 hundreds $\div$ 2

6 Which number makes the following equation true?

$$\square \div 7 = 300$$

- (F) 21
- (G) 210
- (H) 2,100
- (J) 21,000

7 Which number makes the following equation true?

$$\square \div 3 = 1,300$$

- (A) 3,900
- (B) 9,300
- (C) 39,000
- (D) 93,000

8 Herbert is taking a trip to Yellowstone National Park. The park is 1,600 miles from his house in Roanoke. If he drives 400 miles a day, how many days will it take him to reach Yellowstone Park?

- (F) 4
- (G) 6
- (H) 8
- (J) 12

Lesson 11-4   Name _____

1 **Estimate the quotient.**

$$66 \div 9$$

Ⓐ 3   Ⓒ 7

Ⓑ 6   Ⓓ 8

2 **Estimate the quotient.**

$$39 \div 5$$

Ⓕ 5   Ⓗ 8

Ⓖ 7   Ⓙ 9

3 **Estimate the quotient.**

$$50 \div 7$$

Ⓐ 6

Ⓑ 7

Ⓒ 9

Ⓓ 10

4 **Which division fact would you use to estimate the quotient 44 ÷ 5?**

Ⓕ $44 \div 4$

Ⓖ $45 \div 9$

Ⓗ $45 \div 5$

Ⓙ $44 \div 2$

5 **Susan has 6 pins, and her friend Katrina has 50 pins. About how many times more pins does Katrina have than Susan?**

Ⓐ 8

Ⓑ 9

Ⓒ 10

Ⓓ 11

6 **A box of pretzel sticks has 35 pretzels in it. There are 8 boys. About how many pretzels does each boy get?**

Ⓕ 3

Ⓖ 4

Ⓗ 5

Ⓙ 6

7 **There are 71 students going on a field trip. A school rule states that, on field trips, there must be at least 1 adult chaperone per 9 students. Which of the following shows the least number of chaperones that must go on this trip?**

Ⓐ 7   Ⓒ 9

Ⓑ 8   Ⓓ 10

8 **Steven had 34 pennies. He placed an equal number in 4 jars. Jane estimated that each jar contained 10 pennies. Was she correct or incorrect? If she was incorrect, what is a better estimate of the number of pennies each jar contains?**

SOL 3.10 The student will represent multiplication ... using area and set models, and ... solve problems that involve multiplication of two whole numbers, one factor 99 or less and the second factor 5 or less.

Lesson 11-5   Name _____

1 What is 3 × 13? Use the array of place-value blocks below to help you answer the question.

- (A) 33
- (B) 39
- (C) 49
- (D) 53

2 In Carrie's school, there are 4 classrooms, each with 18 students. How many students in all attend Carrie's school? Use the array of place-value blocks below to help you answer this question.

- (F) 64
- (G) 72
- (H) 80
- (J) 96

3 What is 3 × 26? Use the array of place-value blocks below to help you answer the question.

- (A) 78
- (B) 86
- (C) 94
- (D) 98

4 Carla, Stacey, and Sue all work at the ice cream shop. The hours they worked in one week are shown in the table.

Name	Hours Worked
Carla	23
Stacey	27
Sue	14

If each is paid $4 per hour, how much money did Stacey make this week?

- (F) $48
- (G) $56
- (H) $92
- (J) $108

5 What is 3 × 49?

- (A) 129
- (B) 137
- (C) 147
- (D) 156

6 What is 4 × 76?

- (F) 272
- (G) 285
- (H) 304
- (J) 316

Lesson 11-6   Name _____

1 Find the product.

$$3 \times 89$$

Ⓐ 207

Ⓑ 227

Ⓒ 247

Ⓓ 267

2 Find the product.

$$4 \times 98$$

Ⓕ 392

Ⓖ 472

Ⓗ 492

Ⓙ 512

3 Find the product.

$$2 \times 85$$

Ⓐ 160

Ⓑ 170

Ⓒ 180

Ⓓ 190

4 What is the first step in finding the product of 7×35?

Ⓕ Multiply 7×5.

Ⓖ Multiply 7×3.

Ⓗ Multiply 7×30.

Ⓙ Multiply 7×50.

5 In the gym at Portsmouth Middle School there are 4 sets of bleachers, each of which holds 48 students. How many students can sit on the bleachers in the gym?

Ⓐ 94

Ⓑ 96

Ⓒ 182

Ⓓ 192

6 There are 5 baseball teams in the Richmond area. Each team has 19 players. What is the total number of baseball players in the Richmond area on those teams?

Ⓕ 94

Ⓖ 95

Ⓗ 98

Ⓙ 102

7 What number could be placed in the equation to make it true?

$$3 \times 92 = \square$$

Ⓐ 256

Ⓑ 276

Ⓒ 296

Ⓓ 306

SOL 3.10 The student will represent multiplication ... using area and set models, and ... solve problems that involve multiplication of two whole numbers, one factor 99 or less and the second factor 5 or less.

Lesson 11-7   Name _____

1 Find the product. Use models.

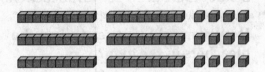

$$24 \times 3 =$$

Ⓐ 48   Ⓒ 72

Ⓑ 62   Ⓓ 612

2 Find the product.

$$3 \times 93$$

Ⓕ 179   Ⓗ 279

Ⓖ 197   Ⓙ 297

3 Find the product.

$$5 \times 58$$

Ⓐ 250   Ⓒ 280

Ⓑ 260   Ⓓ 290

4 Find the product.

$$4 \times 75$$

Ⓕ 200

Ⓖ 225

Ⓗ 275

Ⓙ 300

5 Claire has 4 cans of orange juice. Each can contains 12 ounces of juice. How many ounces of juice does Claire have?

Ⓐ 24   Ⓒ 48

Ⓑ 36   Ⓓ 54

6 Andrew delivers the newspaper to 67 customers each day from Monday to Friday. On Sundays, he delivers the paper to 3 times that number of customers. How many people does Andrew deliver the paper to on Sundays?

Ⓕ 191   Ⓗ 211

Ⓖ 201   Ⓙ 221

7 Marcos counted the number of television ads in each 10-minute block of a movie he watched on television. There were 2 ads per 10-minute block. The movie lasted 2 hours. How many ads did he see?

Ⓐ 20   Ⓒ 40

Ⓑ 24   Ⓓ 80

8 Find the product of 4 × 49. Explain how you can break apart the numbers to multiply.

Lesson 11-8   Name _____

1
$$\begin{array}{r} 784 \\ \times\ 5 \\ \hline \end{array}$$

- Ⓐ 392
- Ⓑ 3,520
- Ⓒ 3,900
- Ⓓ 3,920

2
$$\begin{array}{r} 319 \\ \times\ 8 \\ \hline \end{array}$$

- Ⓕ 2,452
- Ⓖ 2,482
- Ⓗ 2,552
- Ⓙ 2,582

3
$$\begin{array}{r} 407 \\ \times\ 9 \\ \hline \end{array}$$

- Ⓐ 3,603
- Ⓑ 3,663
- Ⓒ 3,664
- Ⓓ 4,263

4
$$\begin{array}{r} 333 \\ \times\ 7 \\ \hline \end{array}$$

- Ⓕ 2,121
- Ⓖ 2,131
- Ⓗ 2,311
- Ⓙ 2,331

5 It is 193 miles, from Washington, D.C. to Norfolk, Virginia. Mishka and his parents drive from Norfolk, to Washington, D.C. and back. How many miles did they drive?

- Ⓐ 386
- Ⓑ 296
- Ⓒ 314
- Ⓓ 324

6 The field of Bert's school is a perfect square. Each of the 4 sides is 232 feet long. What is the perimeter of the field at Bert's school?

- Ⓕ 828 feet
- Ⓖ 928 feet
- Ⓗ 1,028 feet
- Ⓙ 1,228 feet

7 African elephants in the wild eat about 770 pounds of food per day; in the form of green grass, shrubs, trees, and other vegetation. If an elephant eats 770 pounds for 5 days, how many pounds of food will it have eaten?

- Ⓐ 3,650
- Ⓑ 3,850
- Ⓒ 3,950
- Ⓓ 4,250

Lesson 11-9   Name _____

1 $2.45
     × 7

Ⓐ $14.85

Ⓑ $16.15

Ⓒ $16.85

Ⓓ $17.15

2 $3.08
     × 4

Ⓕ $12.24

Ⓖ $12.32

Ⓗ $13.32

Ⓙ $120.32

3 $1.99
     × 5

Ⓐ $5.99

Ⓑ $9.95

Ⓒ $9.99

Ⓓ $10.00

4 $5.26
     × 8

Ⓕ $40.68

Ⓖ $41.08

Ⓗ $41.68

Ⓙ $42.08

5 Cathy wanted to buy a slice of pizza for two friends and herself. Slices of pizza at the Roanoke House of Pizza cost $1.60. How much would it cost her to buy pizza for the 3 of them?

Ⓐ $4.80

Ⓑ $4.90

Ⓒ $5.20

Ⓓ $5.40

6 A boat tour around the Portsmouth harbor costs $3.25. If 6 friends would like to take the tour together, how much would be the total cost for this group?

Ⓕ $18.00

Ⓖ $18.50

Ⓗ $19.00

Ⓙ $19.50

7 Lori's mother asked her to buy 4 pounds of walnuts at the store. Walnuts are $5.06 per pound. Which is the least amount of money Lori's mother should give her to buy the walnuts?

Ⓐ $15.00

Ⓑ $20.00

Ⓒ $21.00

Ⓓ $25.00

Lesson 11-10   Name _____

1 Margaret and Noel are planning a trip to Norfolk. They buy two plane tickets, each of which costs $186. How much do their tickets cost, altogether?

Ⓐ $232

Ⓑ $272

Ⓒ $322

Ⓓ $372

2 Kate drinks 3 glasses of water every day of the year. How many glasses of water does she drink in a year?

Ⓕ 730

Ⓖ 1,080

Ⓗ 1,095

Ⓙ 1,098

3 Ms. Hill is planting 125 bulbs in each of 4 plots of garden around her house. How many bulbs will she have planted when she is done?

Ⓐ 500

Ⓑ 550

Ⓒ 600

Ⓓ 650

4 Darcie wants to send four packages to pen pals that she has around the country. Each of the packages will cost $1.78 to mail. How much will it cost her to mail all four packages?

Ⓕ $6.12

Ⓖ $7.12

Ⓗ $7.42

Ⓙ $7.82

5 The fair at Varney Field lasts for 5 days. On each day of the fair, the parking lot will be full. The lot can hold 198 cars. What is the total number of cars that will park in the parking lot during the fair?

Ⓐ 890

Ⓑ 900

Ⓒ 990

Ⓓ 1,000

6 What is 3,021 × 4?

Ⓕ 8,840

Ⓖ 10,084

Ⓗ 11,084

Ⓙ 12,084

7 In Charlottesville, each city bus can hold 89 people. How many people can 4 buses hold? Describe the method you would use to solve this problem, and why you chose this method.

_____

_____

Lesson 11-11   Name _____

1 The first doctor appointment of the day is at 10:00 and the last is at 2:00. Jessica's appointment is not the first one of the day nor the last. Jessica's appointment is on the hour. The sum of the digits in the hour is 2. What time is Jessica's appointment?

(A) Ten o'clock

(B) Eleven o'clock

(C) Noon

(D) One o'clock

2 Bart's grandfather is 8 times as old as Bart. Bart's father is 28 years younger than his grandfather. Bart is 8 years old. How old is Bart's father?

(F) 20   (H) 36

(G) 28   (J) 64

3 What is the date that the school play is being held? Use the clues.

November						
S	M	T	W	T	F	S
	1	2	3	4	5	6
7	8	9	10	11	12	13
14	15	16	17	18	19	20
21	22	23	24	25	26	27
28	29	30				

1. The school play is on a weekend night.
2. The date has two digits.
3. The sum of the digits is 5.

(A) November 11th

(B) November 13th

(C) November 14th

(D) November 23rd

4 Use the table below to figure out who got an A⁺ on the math test. Only one student got each grade.

	Paola	Liza	Eddie	Dale
A⁺		No		
A	No	Yes	No	No
B⁺		No		
B		No		

1. Liza got an A.
2. Eddie did not get a B⁺.
3. Dale got a B.

(F) Paola   (H) Eddie

(G) Liza   (J) Dale

5 Maggie is at the front of the line. Bill is after Maggie but before Jeremy. Dale is behind Jeremy. Which student is second in line?

(A) Bill   (C) Jeremy

(B) Maggie   (D) Mark

6 On Ted's street, the number on the first house on his side of the street is 301. The next house in on the same side of the street is 303, and the one next to it is 305. The last house on that side of the street has the number 315. Following this pattern, how many houses are there on his side of the street?

(F) 7   (H) 9

(G) 8   (J) 10

Lesson 11-12   Name _____

1 Which division sentence is shown by the place-value blocks below?

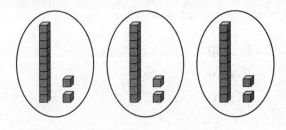

Ⓐ 12 × 3 = 36

Ⓑ 12 ÷ 3 = 4

Ⓒ 36 × 3 = 108

Ⓓ 36 ÷ 3 = 12

2 Use the place-value blocks below to find the quotient 78 ÷ 3.

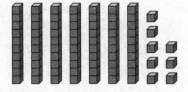

Ⓕ 26

Ⓖ 28

Ⓗ 30

Ⓙ 32

3 Use place-value blocks to find the missing term in the equation below:

$$56 \div \boxed{} = 7$$

Ⓐ 5   Ⓒ 7

Ⓑ 6   Ⓓ 8

Use place-value blocks or draw a picture for 4–6.

4 Patricia's mother bought her 4 new shirts just before school started. Her mother spent $76 on the shirts. All of the shirts cost the same amount. How much did each shirt cost?

Ⓕ $13

Ⓖ $17

Ⓗ $19

Ⓙ $21

5 A container of low fat yogurt contains a total of 72 calories. If the container says that there are 4 servings in the container, how many calories would each serving contain?

Ⓐ 18

Ⓑ 20

Ⓒ 22

Ⓓ 24

6 Sasha collected 6 times as many twigs for the campfire as Sharon. Sasha collected 72 twigs. How many twigs did Sharon collect?

Ⓕ 8

Ⓖ 9

Ⓗ 10

Ⓙ 12

149

Lesson 11-13   Name _____

1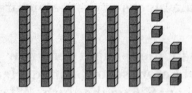

$$68 \div 4 =$$

Ⓐ 13

Ⓑ 15

Ⓒ 17

Ⓓ 19

2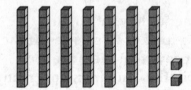

$$72 \div 3 =$$

Ⓕ 24

Ⓖ 26

Ⓗ 28

Ⓙ 30

You may use a drawing for 3–4.

3 Use the break-apart method to divide the number below:

$$48 \div 4 = \square$$

Ⓐ 6   Ⓒ 10

Ⓑ 8   Ⓓ 12

4 Use the break-apart method to divide the number below:

$$44 \div 4$$

Ⓕ 48

Ⓖ 40

Ⓗ 11

Ⓙ 10

5 Which division sentence does the model show?

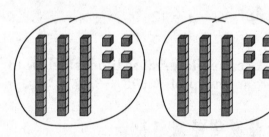

Ⓐ $36 \div 2 = 18$

Ⓑ $36 \div 6 = 6$

Ⓒ $72 \div 2 = 36$

Ⓓ $72 \div 3 = 24$

6 Which steps would you use to find $69 \div 3$?

Ⓕ $60 \div 3 = 20, 9 \div 3 = 3, 20 + 3 = 23$

Ⓖ $60 \div 2 = 15, 9 \div 3 = 3, 15 + 3 = 18$

Ⓗ $60 \div 6 = 10, 9 \div 3 = 3, 10 + 3 = 13$

Ⓙ $60 \div 3 = 20, 9 \div 9 = 1, 20 + 1 = 21$

7 What is the quotient of $38 \div 2$? Describe how you can use breaking apart to solve this problem.

_____

_____

Lesson 11-14   Name _____

1   7)52

Ⓐ 7
Ⓑ 7 R2
Ⓒ 7 R3
Ⓓ 8

2   4)30

Ⓕ 7
Ⓖ 7 R2
Ⓗ 7 R3
Ⓙ 8

3   5)66

Ⓐ 11
Ⓑ 11 R5
Ⓒ 13
Ⓓ 13 R1

4   4)82

Ⓕ 2 R2
Ⓖ 20 R2
Ⓗ 22
Ⓙ 23

5   9)83

Ⓐ 9
Ⓑ 9 R1
Ⓒ 9 R2
Ⓓ 9 R3

6   3)29

Ⓕ 10
Ⓖ 9 R2
Ⓗ 9 R1
Ⓙ 9

7   8)36

Ⓐ 4
Ⓑ 4 R3
Ⓒ 4 R4
Ⓓ 5 R4

8   How do you check $37 \div 5 = 7$ R2?

Ⓕ $8 \times 5 = 40, 40 - 3 = 37$
Ⓖ $7 \times 5 = 35, 35 + 2 = 37$
Ⓗ $7 \times 5 = 35$
Ⓙ $37 \div 7 = 5$ R2

9   How do you check $73 \div 4 = 18$ R1?

Ⓐ $4 \times (18 + 1) = 76$
Ⓑ $(4 \times 18) - 2 = 71$
Ⓒ $(4 \times 18) + 1 = 73$
Ⓓ $(7 \times 10) + 3 = 73$

Lesson 11-15   Name _____

1 Trisha mows lawns in her neighborhood. It takes her 4 hours to mow one lawn. She wants to work 25 hours a week. How many lawns can she mow per week?

(A) 6

(B) 7

(C) 8

(D) 9

2 Keera is making skirts for herself. She needs 5 yards of material for each skirt. She has a total of 37 yards of material. How many yards of material will be left over after she has made all of the skirts that she can?

(F) 1

(G) 2

(H) 3

(J) 4

3 Keith buys 47 tennis balls and puts them into containers that hold three balls each. How many containers will be full of tennis balls?

(A) 11

(B) 12

(C) 13

(D) 15

4 Mrs. Mercer bought a box of 32 oranges. There are 5 people in her family. If everyone eats the same number of oranges, how many oranges will they each have eaten?

(F) 4

(G) 5

(H) 6

(J) 7

5 Hot dogs come in packs of 6, and hot dog buns come in packs of 8. If Harry buys 6 packs of hot dogs, how many packs of hot dog buns will he need?

(A) 3

(B) 4

(C) 5

(D) 6

6 In one week, Carrie ran a total of 27 miles. She ran the same number of miles every day of the week except Sunday. On Sunday she ran 3 miles. How many miles did she run on the other days?

(F) 2

(G) 3

(H) 4

(J) 5

Lesson 11-16   Name _____

1 Carla drove 373 miles one week and 449 miles the next week. How many miles did she drive in those two weeks?

Ⓐ 76

Ⓑ 722

Ⓒ 812

Ⓓ 822

2 One day Frank consumed 2,876 calories and Wayne consumed 1,805 calories. About how many calories did the boys consume together?

Ⓕ 3,000

Ⓖ 4,000

Ⓗ 5,000

Ⓙ 6,000

3 Three classes are going on a field trip to the Natural History Museum. Each van can hold 16 people, and the classes are made up of 23, 25, and 28 students. How many vans will the classes need to take to the Natural History museum?

Ⓐ 4   Ⓒ 6

Ⓑ 5   Ⓓ 7

4 The elementary school library has 1,625 books. The secondary school library has 2,375 books. How many books do the two libraries have in all?

Ⓕ 3,000

Ⓖ 3,975

Ⓗ 3,990

Ⓙ 4,000

5 Sandra needs to read two books for class. One book is 168 pages long. The other is 483 pages long. How many pages does Sandra need to read?

Ⓐ 315

Ⓑ 551

Ⓒ 641

Ⓓ 651

6 The sum of three numbers is 8,716. Two of the numbers are 3,522 and 1,475. What is the third?

Ⓕ 3,719

Ⓖ 4,997

Ⓗ 5,194

Ⓙ 7,241

7 Find the sum of 2,998 and 1,345. Explain the method you used.

_____

_____

Lesson 12-1   Name _____

1 Which is the MOST LIKELY amount of water that the watering can will hold when full?

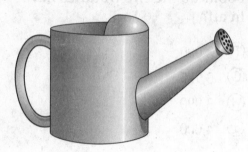

├─ 10 inches ─┤

- Ⓐ 1 pint
- Ⓑ 1 gram
- Ⓒ 1 cup
- Ⓓ 1 gallon

2 Amy wants to divide 2 gallons of orange juice into quart containers. How many quarts can be filled with orange juice?

- Ⓕ 4
- Ⓖ 8
- Ⓗ 12
- Ⓙ 16

3 There are 32 students in Mr. Alcott's class. Mr. Alcott gives each student one cup of apple juice at lunchtime. How many gallons of apple juice will he need?

- Ⓐ 2
- Ⓑ 4
- Ⓒ 6
- Ⓓ 8

4 Cooper and his two brothers are filling up their new goldfish bowl with water. Cooper puts in 2 pints of water, Tom puts in 4 cups of water, and Stefan puts in 2 quarts of water. How much water is in the goldfish bowl when they are done filling the bowl?

- Ⓕ 1 gallon
- Ⓖ 2 gallons
- Ⓗ 3 gallons
- Ⓙ 4 gallons

5 Which is the MOST LIKELY amount of water that the glass can hold?

- Ⓐ 1 cup
- Ⓑ 1 pint
- Ⓒ 1 quart
- Ⓓ 1 gallon

6 How many cups are there in one quart?

- Ⓕ 2
- Ⓖ 4
- Ⓗ 8
- Ⓙ 16

Lesson 12-2   Name _____

1 Louise has a 2-liter bottle of orange juice. How many milliliters of orange juice are in the 2-liter bottle?

- Ⓐ 200
- Ⓑ 2,000
- Ⓒ 400
- Ⓓ 4,000

2 Tanya gave her mother a bottle of perfume. What is the BEST estimate of how much perfume is in the bottle?

- Ⓕ 1 milliliter
- Ⓖ 100 milliliters
- Ⓗ 1 liter
- Ⓙ 10 liters

3 Which is the MOST LIKELY amount of water that a bathtub can hold?

- Ⓐ 40 milliliters
- Ⓑ 400 milliliters
- Ⓒ 40 liters
- Ⓓ 400 liters

4 James had a one-liter bottle of water. He drank 450 milliliters of the water. How much of the water was left?

- Ⓕ 50 milliliters
- Ⓖ 150 milliliters
- Ⓗ 450 milliliters
- Ⓙ 550 milliliters

5 Which is the MOST LIKELY amount of paint in the paint can?

- Ⓐ 4 milliliters
- Ⓒ 4 liters
- Ⓑ 40 milliliters
- Ⓓ 40 liters

6 A pitcher holds 6 liters of water. The water is evenly divided among 8 people. How many milliliters of water will each person get?

- Ⓕ 550 milliliters
- Ⓖ 650 milliliters
- Ⓗ 750 milliliters
- Ⓙ 850 milliliters

7 Barbara has two 2-liter bottles of water. How many milliliters of water is this? Explain how you can use mental math to change between liters and milliliters.

Lesson 12-3   Name _____

1 It took Britt 30 minutes to walk from his house to Jim's house. Then it took him 25 minutes for him to walk to the movie theater. He arrived at the movie theater at 4:15 P.M. What time did Britt leave his house?

Ⓐ 3:00 P.M.

Ⓑ 3:10 P.M.

Ⓒ 3:20 P.M.

Ⓓ 3:30 P.M.

2 Jason, Kori, Mark, and Jim are waiting in line to give blood at the local Red Cross. Kori is in front of Jason. Mark is between Kori and Jason. Jim is last. Who will be first to give blood?

Ⓕ Jason

Ⓖ Kori

Ⓗ Mark

Ⓙ Jim

3 Cathy, Molly, or Dave can be hall monitor, eraser cleaner, or homework collector. How many ways can the 3 students be picked for the 3 different jobs?

Ⓐ 6

Ⓑ 9

Ⓒ 11

Ⓓ 13

4 Ben cut a long piece of string into two equal pieces. He then cut 3 inches off of one of the pieces. After he cut this piece, the remainder was 5 inches long. How long was the original string?

Ⓕ 10 inches

Ⓖ 12 inches

Ⓗ 14 inches

Ⓙ 16 inches

5 At the book store, Barbara spent $1.75 on notecards and $2.75 for a magazine. After buying these items, she had $5.00 left. How much did she have before she bought the items?

Ⓐ $9.50

Ⓑ $9.75

Ⓒ $10.25

Ⓓ $10.50

6 Victoria had a total of 33 index cards. She gave 17 of them away and received 12 more. How many index cards did Victoria have?

Ⓕ 18

Ⓖ 24

Ⓗ 28

Ⓙ 32

Lesson 12-4   Name _____

1 The cat in the picture MOST LIKELY weighs —

- (A) 10 ounces
- (B) 10 pounds
- (C) 40 ounces
- (D) 40 pounds

2 Brian's new puppy weighs 6 pounds. How many ounces does his puppy weigh?

- (F) 64
- (G) 72
- (H) 84
- (J) 96

3 Karen's toy bear weighs 9 ounces and Jill's toy giraffe weighs 1 pound, 4 ounces. How much more does Jill's giraffe weigh?

- (A) 11 ounces
- (B) 13 ounces
- (C) 15 ounces
- (D) 17 ounces

4 The scissors in the picture MOST LIKELY weighs —

- (F) 4 ounces
- (G) 4 pounds
- (H) 20 ounces
- (J) 20 pounds

5 A bag of California oranges at the grocery store costs $3.20 per pound. How much do these oranges cost per ounce?

- (A) 0.2¢
- (B) 2¢
- (C) 20¢
- (D) $2.00

6 Travis buys a 22-ounce bag of cashew nuts at the corner store. How many pounds and ounces of cashew nuts did he buy?

- (F) 1 pound 2 ounces
- (G) 1 pound 4 ounces
- (H) 1 pound 6 ounces
- (J) 1 pound 8 ounces

7 How many pounds are there in 34 ounces? How many ounces are left over? Explain your answer.

_____

Lesson 12-5   Name _____

1 Which is the apple about as heavy as?

Ⓐ 20 grams

Ⓑ 200 grams

Ⓒ 1 kilogram

Ⓓ 10 kilograms

2 John buys two bags of apples at the orchard. One of the bags of apples is as heavy as 2,650 grams and the other bag of apples is as heavy as 1,350 grams. How many kilograms are the bags as heavy as altogether?

Ⓕ 0.5 kilograms

Ⓖ 1 kilogram

Ⓗ 4 kilograms

Ⓙ 7 kilograms

3 Louise, Frank, and Maggie picked up pine cones from the lawn. Louise picked up 300 grams of pine cones, Frank picked up 700 grams of pine cones, and Maggie picked up 2 kilograms of pine cones. How heavy were all the pine cones together?

Ⓐ 1 kilogram

Ⓑ 2 kilograms

Ⓒ 3 kilograms

Ⓓ 4 kilograms

4 Joe's dog eats 140 grams of dog food each day. About how much dog food does his dog eat in a week?

Ⓕ 1 kilogram

Ⓖ 3 kilograms

Ⓗ 4 kilograms

Ⓙ 6 kilograms

5 Which is the book about as heavy as?

MATH

Ⓐ 1 gram

Ⓑ 10 grams

Ⓒ 1 kilogram

Ⓓ 10 kilograms

6 The label on a box of crackers says that the entire box of crackers contains 60 grams of fat. Stuart eats one box of crackers a week for 5 months (20 weeks). About how many grams of fat will he have eaten?

Ⓕ 1 kilogram

Ⓖ 2 kilograms

Ⓗ 3 kilograms

Ⓙ 4 kilograms

Lesson 12-6   Name _____

1 Which is the CLOSEST to the Celsius temperature shown on the thermometer?

Ⓐ ⁻6°C

Ⓑ ⁻2°C

Ⓒ 21°C

Ⓓ 22°C

2 Neko wants to go swimming in the lake near her house. Which water temperature would make her swim the most enjoyable?

Ⓕ 30°F

Ⓖ 30°C

Ⓗ 100°F

Ⓙ 100°C

3 When Carrie woke up, at 6:30 A.M., it was 32°F. When she left school for the day, at 2:00 P.M., the temperature had risen to 56°F. How much did the temperature increase while she was at school?

Ⓐ 20°F

Ⓑ 22°F

Ⓒ 24°F

Ⓓ 26°F

4 Carl lives near Virginia Beach. As he leaves for school one day, he notices that the thermometer on the side of his house reads 12°F. Which is the MOST LIKELY season on that day?

Ⓕ Summer

Ⓖ Fall

Ⓗ Winter

Ⓙ Spring

5 Which of the following is the CLOSEST to the Fahrenheit temperature shown on the thermometer?

Ⓐ 32°F

Ⓑ 48°F

Ⓒ 90°F

Ⓓ 100°F

6 Jack writes his pen pal from South America. He tells her that in Richmond, Virginia, it is 11°C, and she writes back and says that in her city it is 45°C. What is the difference in temperature between the two cities?

Ⓕ 24°C

Ⓖ 34°C

Ⓗ 56°C

Ⓙ 66°C

Lesson 12-7   Name _____

1 Christopher was picking marbles out of a jar. The jar contained 37 red marbles, 4 blue marbles, and 3 green marbles. Which best describes Christopher's chances for choosing a red marble?

   Ⓐ Likely   Ⓒ Unlikely

   Ⓑ Certain   Ⓓ Impossible

2 Nicole bought these vegetables at the grocery store.

If Nicole picks one vegetable from the bag without looking, which kind of vegetable is she LEAST LIKELY to pick?

   Ⓕ Celery   Ⓗ Lettuce

   Ⓖ Carrot   Ⓙ Tomato

3 You are about to toss a cube numbered from 1 to 6. Which describes the chances that you will toss a 3?

   Ⓐ Impossible   Ⓒ Likely

   Ⓑ Certain   Ⓓ Unlikely

4 Which is the spinner LEAST LIKELY to land on?

   Ⓕ 1   Ⓗ 3

   Ⓖ 2   Ⓙ 4

5 Greg has a pet salamander named Bert. What is the likelihood that Bert will learn to play the harmonica?

   Ⓐ Likely

   Ⓑ Certain

   Ⓒ Unlikely

   Ⓓ Impossible

6 The table below shows the number of shirts that Mark, Eddie, Scott, and Michelle gave to charity.

Name	Number of Shirts
Mark	4
Eddie	2
Scott	8
Michelle	17

If you reached into the bag of shirts given to charity, whose shirt would you be MOST LIKELY to pick?

   Ⓕ Mark's   Ⓗ Scott's

   Ⓖ Eddie's   Ⓙ Michelle's

Lesson 12-8   Name _____

1   What are the chances that the spinner will land on 3?

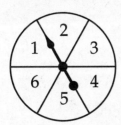

Ⓐ   1 out of 2   Ⓒ   1 out of 6
Ⓑ   2 out of 3   Ⓓ   3 out of 6

2   The captains of two volleyball teams are choosing players. All of the students in the class write their names on pieces of paper and the captains of the two volley ball teams take turns drawing. What is the chance that the first captain to choose will draw a boy's name?

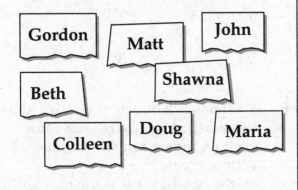

Ⓕ   3 out of 8   Ⓗ   3 out of 9
Ⓖ   4 out of 8   Ⓙ   4 out of 9

3   Ann has a cube that has sides numbered 1, 2, 3, 4, 5, and 6. What are the chances of her rolling a number that is 4 or less?

Ⓐ   2 out of 6   Ⓒ   4 out of 6
Ⓑ   3 out of 6   Ⓓ   5 out of 6

4   What is the chance of the spinner landing on black?

Ⓕ   1 in 6   Ⓗ   2 in 6
Ⓖ   1 in 2   Ⓙ   3 in 6

5   If all of the cards below were face-down on the table, what would be the chances of picking up an 'A'?

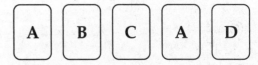

Ⓐ   1 out of 5   Ⓒ   3 out of 5
Ⓑ   2 out of 5   Ⓓ   4 out of 5

6   The following bags contain 10 black and white marbles. If you draw one marble out of one of the bags, which bag would give you a 1 in 5 chance of drawing a black marble?

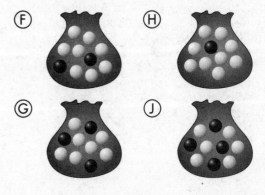

Lesson 12-9   Name _____

1 A number cube has the numbers 5, 11, 15, 20, 24, and 27 on its sides. Which of the following is the probability of tossing the cube and getting an odd number?

Ⓐ $\frac{1}{6}$ Ⓒ $\frac{3}{6}$

Ⓑ $\frac{2}{6}$ Ⓓ $\frac{4}{6}$

2 Tor has 5 black playing cards, numbered 1, 2, 3, 4, and 5, and 5 red playing cards, also numbered 1, 2, 3, 4, and 5. He chose one card at random. What is the probability that he chose a red 4?

Ⓕ $\frac{1}{10}$

Ⓖ $\frac{2}{10}$

Ⓗ $\frac{4}{10}$

Ⓙ $\frac{5}{10}$

3 What is the probability of picking a black marble out of the bag of marbles shown?

Ⓐ $\frac{1}{9}$ Ⓒ $\frac{5}{9}$

Ⓑ $\frac{3}{9}$ Ⓓ $\frac{6}{9}$

4 What is the probability of spinning an odd number?

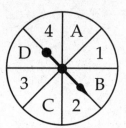

Ⓕ $\frac{1}{10}$ Ⓗ $\frac{1}{8}$

Ⓖ $\frac{2}{10}$ Ⓙ $\frac{2}{8}$

5 What is the probability of choosing a card that is LESS THAN 5 but GREATER THAN 2?

| 1 | 2 | 3 | 4 | 5 | 6 |

Ⓐ $\frac{1}{6}$ Ⓒ $\frac{3}{6}$

Ⓑ $\frac{2}{6}$ Ⓓ $\frac{4}{6}$

6 Kristen has a bunch of elastic bands in a plastic bag. There are 8 blue elastic bands, 6 red elastic bands, 4 yellow elastic bands, and 5 green elastic bands. What is the probability that she will reach into the bag and take out a blue elastic band?

Ⓕ $\frac{4}{23}$ Ⓗ $\frac{6}{23}$

Ⓖ $\frac{5}{23}$ Ⓙ $\frac{8}{23}$

Lesson 12-10   Name _____

1 Students in Mr. Hamm's class voted on their favorite juice: grape, apple, orange or cranberry.

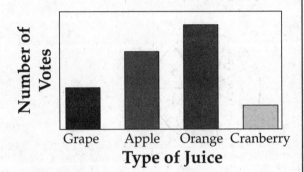

Type of Juice

Which was the favorite?

Ⓐ Grape

Ⓑ Apple

Ⓒ Orange

Ⓓ Cranberry

2 Adam predicted that in 50 spins he would spin white more times than he would spin black. Which of the spinners below is Adam's spinner?

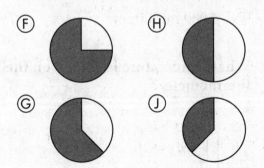

3 Bridget took one fruit from the bag, recorded its type, and then put it back in the bag. She did this 50 times. The table shows the results.

Peach	Plum	Tangerine
4	12	34

Which is CLOSEST to the number of fruits in the bag?

Ⓐ 8 peaches, 1 plum, 1 tangerine

Ⓑ 4 peaches, 4 plums, 2 tangerines

Ⓒ 8 tangerines, 3 plums, 1 peach

Ⓓ 8 tangerines, 1 plum, 1 peach

4 Libby has a cube numbered from 1 to 6. She rolls the cube 100 times. Which is the BEST prediction of the fraction of times she will roll an even number?

Ⓕ $\frac{20}{100}$ Ⓗ $\frac{50}{100}$

Ⓖ $\frac{40}{100}$ Ⓙ $\frac{60}{100}$

5 Peter predicted that if he spun this spinner 100 times, it would land on N as often as it landed on M. Do you agree or disagree? Explain.

Lesson 12-11   Name _____

1 The school cafeteria ordered 10 gallons of orange juice. How many quarts of orange juice is that?

- Ⓐ 40
- Ⓑ 80
- Ⓒ 120
- Ⓓ 160

2 There are three colors of buttons in a plastic bag. There are 28 blue, 12 red, and 20 green buttons. If Brian reaches into the bag and pulls out one of the buttons, what are the odds that he will get a green button?

- Ⓕ $\frac{12}{60}$
- Ⓖ $\frac{20}{60}$
- Ⓗ $\frac{28}{60}$
- Ⓙ $\frac{20}{48}$

3 Diane spent $6.00 for a movie ticket, $1.25 on a soft drink, and $3.50 on popcorn. Afterwards, she was left with $9.25. How much money did she start with?

- Ⓐ $10.00
- Ⓑ $15.00
- Ⓒ $20.00
- Ⓓ $25.00

4 What is the probability that the spinner will land on a number that is GREATER THAN 5 and LESS THAN 7?

- Ⓕ $\frac{1}{7}$
- Ⓗ $\frac{3}{7}$
- Ⓖ $\frac{2}{7}$
- Ⓙ $\frac{4}{7}$

5 Larry buys a container that holds 4 liters of water. How many milliliters of water does this container hold?

- Ⓐ 200 milliliters
- Ⓑ 400 milliliters
- Ⓒ 2,000 milliliters
- Ⓓ 4,000 milliliters

6 What temperature is shown on the thermometer?

- Ⓕ 14°C
- Ⓖ 44°F
- Ⓗ 44°C
- Ⓙ 56°F

Virginia
SOL Practice Assessments

GRADE 3
MATHEMATICS

Name _____

Date _____

DIRECTIONS
Read and solve each question. Then mark the space on the answer sheet for the best answer.

SAMPLE

Which number on the racecars is an even number?

A 29

B 35

C 48

D 57

1 Jackson baked 64 dog biscuits and Maria baked 25 dog biscuits. How many dog biscuits did they bake in all?

A 39

B 55

C 89

D 98

2 What fraction of the animals are horses?

F $\frac{3}{4}$

G $\frac{1}{3}$

H $\frac{1}{4}$

J $\frac{1}{8}$

GO ON

3 8 × 5 =

  A 13

  B 35

  C 40

  D 85

4 Gina had this money to spend at the Richmond State Fair.

Which treat costs exactly the same as the value of Gina's money?

F $2.80

G $2.60

H $2.50

J $2.40

5 When Sherrie finished grooming her rabbit, her clock showed the following time.

What time was it when she finished grooming her rabbit?

  A 6:00

  B 7:00

  C 8:00

  D 9:00

6 This is a whole.

What is

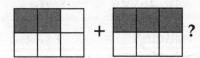

  F $\frac{2}{4}$

  G $\frac{5}{6}$

  H $\frac{4}{8}$

  J $\frac{5}{1}$

GO ON

7 $3 \times 9 =$

Which of the following problems can be solved using the number sentence above?

A Jack had 9 trucks. He gave 3 away. How many trucks did he have left?

B Barbara made 9 sandwiches. If she put 3 sandwiches on each plates, how many plates would she use?

C Gabriel saw 9 blue jays and 3 cardinals. How many birds did she see in all?

D Louis put 9 stamps on each of 3 envelopes. How many stamps did he use in all?

8 **Which list names all the colors Maggie could spin using this spinner?**

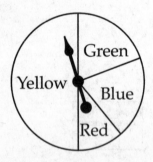

F Green, Yellow, Blue

G Blue, Red, Black, Purple

H Red, Yellow, Green, Blue

J Yellow, Green, Blue, Brown

9 **Which circle is half shaded?**

A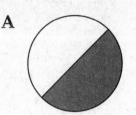

B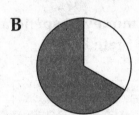

C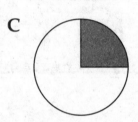

D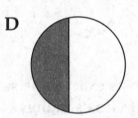

GO ON

10 Tonya made a pictograph of her classmates' favorite cats.

Favorite Cats

Kind of Cat	Number of Votes
Tabby	🐱 🐱 🐱 🐱
Siamese	🐱 🐱 🐱 🐱 🐱
Persian	🐱 🐱
Manx	🐱 🐱 🐱 🐱 🐱

KEY 🐱 = 2 votes.

How many more students chose Manx than Persian?

F 2

G 3

H 6

J 12

11 Find the missing numbers in the pattern.

20, 25, 30, _____, _____, _____

A 30, 40, 50

B 35, 25, 15

C 35, 45, 55

D 35, 40, 45

12 Which temperature would be BEST for swimming at Virginia Beach?

F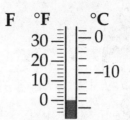

G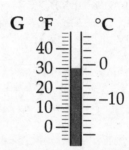

H

J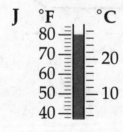

13 Which best describes the chances of the spinner landing on grey?

A Equally likely

B Impossible

C Unlikely

D Certain

14 Use your centimeter ruler to help you answer this question.

What is the length of the pencil shown below to the nearest centimeter?

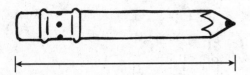

F 3 centimeters

G 6 centimeters

H 9 centimeters

J 12 centimeters

15 How many fish are there in all?

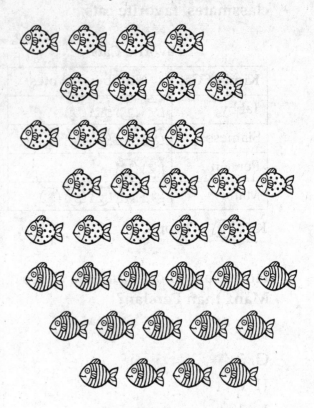

A 22

B 37

C 44

D 50

GO ON

16 What decimal goes in the box to make a true statement?

$$\frac{3}{10} = \boxed{}$$

F 0.03

G 0.3

H 0.7

J 3.0

17 Which symbol goes in the box to make the statement true?

8,700 $\boxed{}$ 7,999

A <

B >

C =

D +

18 Which is CLOSEST to the weight of Doug's sand bucket when it is full of sand?

F 50 pounds

G 2 ounces

H 5 ounces

J 5 pounds

19 Ms. Sanchez drove 39 miles to her meeting. Then she drove 22 miles to the bank. Which is the BEST estimate of how many miles she drove in all?

A 40 miles

B 50 miles

C 60 miles

D 70 miles

GO ON

20 Zora cut an orange into 4 equal pieces. She ate 1 piece.

What fraction tells how much of the orange Zora ate?

F $\frac{1}{8}$

G $\frac{1}{4}$

H $\frac{1}{2}$

J $\frac{3}{4}$

21 Which number makes both of these number sentences true?

$3 \times \square = 15$

$15 \div \square = 3$

A 2

B 3

C 4

D 5

22 A pattern was used to determine the number of spotted tiles and the number of striped tiles in each figure below.

Figure 1

Figure 2

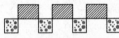

Figure 3

If the pattern continues, how many striped tiles will there be in Figure 5?

F 3

G 5

H 6

J 7

23 Which number makes both of these number sentences true?

$8 + \square = 18$

$18 - \square = 8$

A 8

B 9

C 10

D 11

GO ON

24 What is the value of the underlined 3 in 783,925?

F 300

G 3,000

H 30,000

J 300,000

25 Brittany is making a new chain for her glasses.

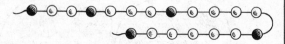

If her pattern continues until it ends with 7 white beads, what is the total number of beads needed to make the chain?

A 19

B 25

C 33

D 49

26 Which is a true number sentence?

F 2 + 5 = 3 + 3

G 3 + 4 = 2 + 8

H 3 + 6 = 2 + 7

J 4 + 5 = 2 + 10

27 This graph shows the results of a classroom vote on their favorite field trips.

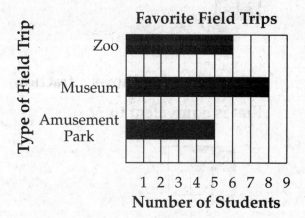

Which of the following statements about the graph is true?

A Two more students voted for the museum than the amusement park.

B Four more students voted for the museum than the zoo.

C A total of 8 students voted on their favorite field trips.

D Three more students voted for the museum than the amusement park.

GO ON

28 The figure below is $\frac{2}{3}$ shaded.

Which drawing shows a fraction that is equivalent to $\frac{2}{3}$?

F

G

H

J

29 Joel drew this picture to find how many seashells he and each of his 3 friends would get if they shared 20 seashells equally.

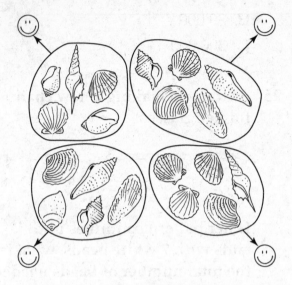

Which number sentence shows how he solved the problem?

A $20 \div 2 = 10$

B $20 \div 4 = 5$

C $20 \div 5 = 4$

D $20 + 4 = 24$

GO ON

30 Bruce wants to make 8 gallons of punch for his party.

How many quarts of punch will he make?

F 12 quarts

G 32 quarts

H 40 quarts

J 64 quarts

31 Keisha is creating a number pattern. She says each number is double the number before it.

3, 6, 12, 24, 48, _____, _____

What are the next two numbers in her pattern?

A 24, 12

B 72, 96

C 96, 192

D 192, 384

32 Carly is making this calendar for her desk.

November						
S	M	T	W	T	F	S
	1	2	3	4	5	6
7	8	9	10	11		

Using her calendar, on what day of the week will November 27 fall?

F Friday

G Saturday

H Sunday

J Monday

33 Glenda drew the following figure on her paper.

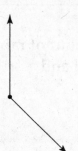

Which best describes her drawing?

A Line segment

B Circle

C Angle

D Square

GO ON

34 The Simpsons drove 978 miles to get to Virginia. Then they drove another 112 miles along the Virginia coastline. How many miles did the Simpsons drive?

F   1,090 miles

G   1,280 miles

H   1,450 miles

J   1,660 miles

35 The table below shows the amount of rain that fell in four cities in one day.

City	Rain (in inches)
Richmond	3.9
Dulles	1.2
Alexandria	1.8
Norfolk	2.5

What is the total amount of rain that fell in Richmond and Norfolk?

A   5.1 inches

B   5.7 inches

C   6.2 inches

D   6.4 inches

36 The next tour of Shenandoah Caverns begins at the time shown on the clock below.

Which does not show the time on the clock?

F   6:55

G   5 minutes before 7

H   55 minutes past 6

J   7:55

37 Janice spent 4 hours making paper cranes. How many minutes are there in 4 hours?

A   40 minutes

B   64 minutes

C   200 minutes

D   240 minutes

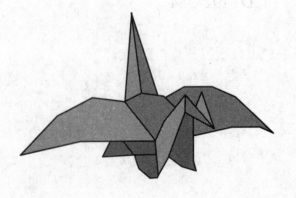

GO ON

38 Mrs. Fox had her students line up for recess. If Amy was 13th in line, which line-up shows Ryan as 16th in line?

F

Amy   Ken   Ryan   Julie   Alex

G

Amy   Ken   Julie   Ryan   Alex

H

Amy   Ryan   Ken   Julie   Alex

J

Amy   Ken   Julie   Alex   Ryan

39 The cafeteria workers made 365 chocolate chip cookies in one day. What is 365 rounded to the nearest hundred?

A 300

B 360

C 370

D 400

40 Which of the following statements about the pictograph is true?

After-School Activities

Kind of Activity	Number of Children
Music	☥ ☥
Art	☥ ☥ ☥ ☥
Sports	☥ ☥ ☥ ☥ ☥ ☥
Scouting	☥ ☥ ☥

KEY ☥ = 2 people.

F More students participate in music than art.

G Scouting is the least popular after-school activity.

H Sports is the most popular after-school activity.

J Fewer students participate in sports than art.

GO ON

41 Which of the shapes below is congruent to the shaded rectangle?

A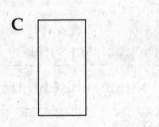

B

C

D

42 Frank is designing a game piece that is a rectangular prism. He plans to write one digit on each side of the prism.

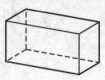

How many digits will he write?

F 4

G 6

H 7

J 8

43 For a week the third-grade classes kept track of the number of cardinals each student saw.

Ms. Carter's class counted 297. Mr. Bie's class counted 314 cardinals. How many cardinals did they count in all that week?

A 516

B 611

C 699

D 727

GO ON

44 Each student in Mrs. Shelby's third grade read books during their winter break. She wrote the number of books they each read on the note card shown below.

Number of Books My Students Read During Break		
3	4	5
8	8	6
4	5	8
8	3	6
6	5	

After she surveyed her students, she started a line plot to show the data.

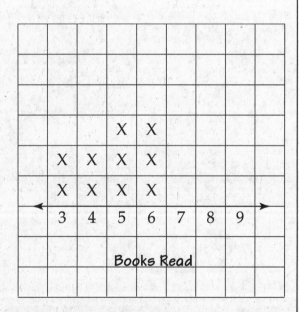

How many Xs should she put above the number 8?

F 2

G 3

H 4

J 5

45 Brianna has an assortment of stickers. Some of her stickers are in her sticker album and some are not. She wants to add the fraction of her stickers that are animal stickers to the fraction of the stickers that are smiley face stickers.

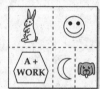

She added $\frac{3}{9} + \frac{2}{9}$ to get her answer. What answer should Brianna get?

A $\frac{5}{9}$

B $\frac{7}{9}$

C $\frac{8}{9}$

D $\frac{9}{5}$

46 What is the value of the underlined 7 in 9<u>7</u>2,834?

   F 70

   G 700

   H 7,000

   J 70,000

47 Which is a true number sentence?

   A $9 - 2 = 8 - 1$

   B $6 - 4 = 10 - 2$

   C $7 - 3 = 8 - 2$

   D $5 - 5 = 9 - 3$

48 Look at the fraction models.

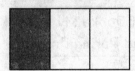

Which statement is true?

   F $\frac{3}{4} = \frac{1}{3}$

   G $\frac{3}{4} < \frac{1}{3}$

   H $\frac{1}{3} < \frac{3}{4}$

   J $\frac{1}{3} > \frac{3}{4}$

GO ON

49 Rob surveyed his friends to determine the most popular shape. Each friend drew his shape on the chalkboard.

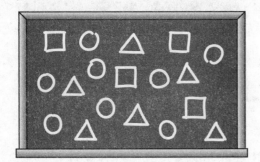

Which graph shows the correct number of each kind of shape?

A

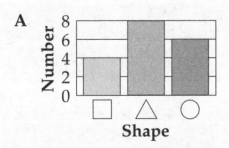

B

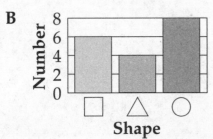

C

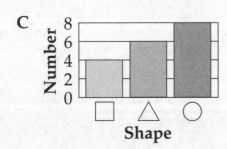

D

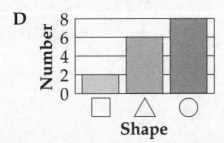

50 Which set of figures continues the pattern?

□ ○ □ ○ □

F   ○ □ ○

G   ○ ○ ○

H   □ □ ○

J   □ ○ □

STOP

Virginia
SOL Practice Assessments

GRADE 3
MATHEMATICS

Name _____

Date _____

DIRECTIONS
Read and solve each question. Then mark the space on the answer sheet for the best answer.

SAMPLE

Which number on the bears is an odd number?

A 36
B 44
C 59
D 62

1   Shari sewed 39 cat toys and Derrick sewed 42 cat toys. How many cat toys did they sew in all?

A 30
B 81
C 88
D 91

2   What fraction of the fish are not spotted?

F $\frac{1}{8}$

G $\frac{1}{4}$

H $\frac{1}{3}$

J $\frac{1}{2}$

3   $7 \times 4 =$

A 11
B 23
C 25
D 28

GO ON

4 Luis had this money to spend at the Virginia Beach snack shack.

Which snack costs exactly the same as the value of Luis' money?

F  $3.90

G  $3.80

H  $3.70

J  $3.60

5 When Julianne finished reading a book about Booker T. Washington, her clock showed the following time.

When did she finish reading her book?

A 6:00

B 7:00

C 8:00

D 9:00

6 This is a whole.

What is

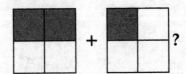 ?

F $\frac{3}{4}$

G $\frac{1}{2}$

H $\frac{3}{8}$

J $\frac{4}{3}$

GO ON

7 2 × 8 =

What problem can be solved using the number sentence above?

A Tom put 8 photos on each of 2 pages. How many photos did he use in all?

B Hannah made 8 cakes. If she put 2 cakes on each tray, how many trays would she use?

C Brad had 8 baseball cards. He gave 2 away. How many baseball cards did he have left?

D Monica drew 8 dogwood trees and 2 oak trees. How many trees did she draw in all?

8 **Which list names all the colors Tara could spin using this spinner?**

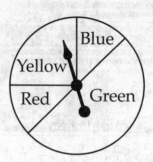

F Red, Yellow, Blue, Purple

G Yellow, Red, Purple, Black

H Blue, Green, Red

J Green, Red, Yellow, Blue

9 **Which rectangle has $\frac{1}{4}$ shaded?**

A

B

C

D

GO ON

10 Jeff made a pictograph of his scout troop's favorite birds.

Favorite Birds

Kind of Bird	Number of Votes
Robins	↞ ↞ ↞
Nuthatches	↞ ↞ ↞ ↞
Crows	↞ ↞
Cardinals	↞ ↞ ↞ ↞ ↞ ↞

KEY ↞ = 2 birds.

How many more scouts chose cardinal than crow?

F 5

G 9

H 10

J 13

11 Find the missing numbers in the pattern.

18, 21, 24, _____, _____, _____

A 26, 28, 30

B 25, 30, 35

C 27, 30, 33

D 28, 32, 36

12 Which temperature would be the BEST for sleigh riding at Shenandoah National Park?

F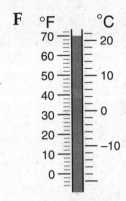

G

H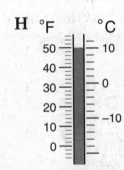

J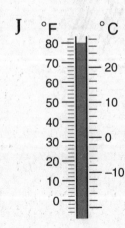

GO ON

13 Which <u>best describes</u> the chances of drawing a spotted marble from the bag?

A Likely

B Impossible

C Unlikely

D Certain

14 Use your centimeter ruler to help you answer this question.

What is the length of the spider shown below to the nearest centimeter?

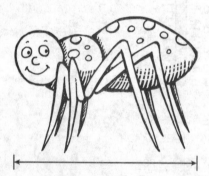

F 2 centimeters

G 3 centimeters

H 4 centimeters

J 5 centimeters

15 How many ties are there in all?

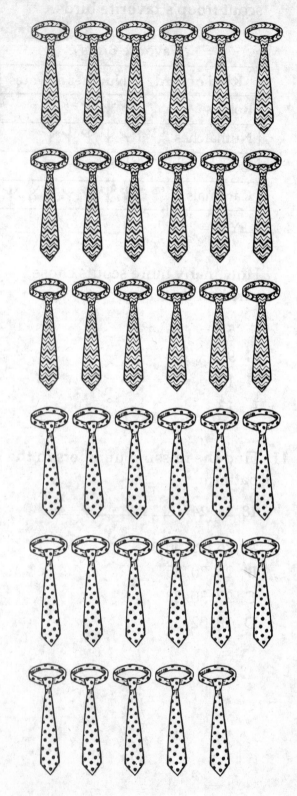

A 18

B 29

C 35

D 39

GO ON

16 What decimal goes in the box to make this a true statement?

$$\frac{7}{10} = \square$$

F 0.07

G 0.3

H 0.7

J 7.0

17 Which symbol goes in the box to make the statement true?

6,582 ☐ 6,601

A <

B >

C =

D +

18 Which is CLOSEST to the weight of Irene's bowling ball?

F 60 pounds

G 16 ounces

H 6 pounds

J 6 ounces

19 Mr. Young drove 43 miles to his conference. Then he drove 19 miles to the hotel. Which is the BEST estimate of how many miles he drove in all?

A 60 miles

B 70 miles

C 80 miles

D 90 miles

GO ON

20 Henry cut a sandwich into 4 equal pieces. He ate 2 pieces.

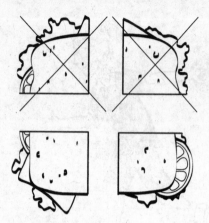

What fraction tells how much of the sandwich Henry ate?

F $\frac{1}{4}$

G $\frac{2}{4}$

H $\frac{3}{4}$

J $\frac{5}{8}$

21 Which number makes both of these number sentences true?

$4 \times \square = 24$
$24 \div \square = 4$

A 3

B 4

C 5

D 6

22 A pattern was used to determine the number of shaded squares and the number of white squares in each figure below.

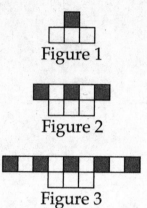

Figure 1

Figure 2

Figure 3

If the pattern continues, how many shaded squares will there be in Figure 5?

F 5

G 7

H 9

J 11

23 Which number makes both of these number sentences true?

$7 + \square = 12$
$12 - \square = 7$

A 3

B 4

C 5

D 7

GO ON

24 What is the value of the underlined 7 in 126,7̲35?

    F 70

    G 700

    H 7,000

    J 70,000

25 Jade is making a beaded necklace.

If her pattern continues until it ends with 6 black beads, what is the total number of beads needed to make the necklace?

    A 24

    B 30

    C 36

    D 42

26 Which is a true number sentence?

    F $3 + 6 = 2 + 9$

    G $2 + 7 = 4 + 3$

    H $4 + 4 = 2 + 9$

    J $7 + 5 = 3 + 9$

27 This graph shows the results of a classroom vote on favorite desserts.

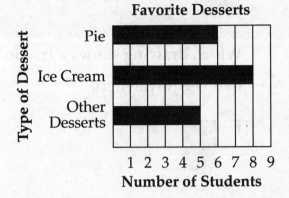

Which of the following statements about the graph is true?

    A Eight students voted for desserts that were not pie or ice cream.

    B Two more students voted for ice cream than pie.

    C Five students voted for pie.

    D A total of 13 students voted on their favorite desserts.

GO ON

28 This figure is $\frac{1}{2}$ shaded.

Which drawing shows a fraction that is equivalent to $\frac{1}{2}$?

F

G

H

J

29 Candice drew this picture to find how many donuts each of her 3 friends would get if they shared 12 donuts equally.

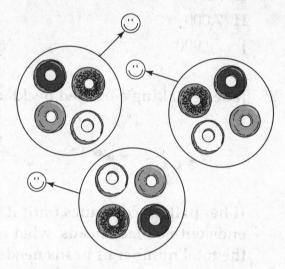

Which division sentence shows how she solved the problem?

A $12 \div 2 = 6$

B $12 \div 3 = 4$

C $12 \div 4 = 3$

D $12 \div 6 = 2$

GO ON

30 Becca wants to make 9 gallons of vegetable soup for Thanksgiving.

How many quarts of vegetable soup will she make?

F   18 quarts

G   27 quarts

H   36 quarts

J   54 quarts

31 Carla is creating a number pattern. Each number is double the number before it.

2, 4, 8, 16, 32, _____, _____

What would be the next two numbers in her pattern?

A   36, 18

B   64, 128

C   72, 144

D   80, 160

32 Levar is making this calendar for his wall.

December						
S	M	T	W	T	F	S
		1	2	3	4	5	6
7	8	9	10	11		

Using his calendar, on what day of the week will December 24 fall?

F   Wednesday

G   Thursday

H   Friday

J   Saturday

33 Roberto drew the following figure on his paper.

●━━━━━●

Which **best describes** his drawing?

A   Circle

B   Square

C   Angle

D   Line segment

34 The Smiths drove 525 miles to get to Virginia. Then they drove another 285 miles to visit some historic sites. How many miles did the Smiths drive in all?

F   240 miles

G   700 miles

H   810 miles

J   1,810 miles

35 The table below shows the amount of snow that fell at four ski resorts in one day.

Resort	Snow (in inches)
Wintergreen	5.2
Massanutten	4.8
Bryce	4.9
Homestead	3.9

What was the total amount of snow that fell in Wintergreen and Bryce?

A   9.9 inches

B   10.1 inches

C   10.5 inches

D   10.8 inches

36 The next film at the Science Museum of Virginia begins at the time shown on the clock below.

Which does not show the time on the clock?

F   4:15

G   45 minutes before 6

H   15 minutes past 5

J   5:15

37 Glen spent 3 hours making pancakes for a breakfast for the homeless. How many minutes are in 3 hours?

A   30 minutes

B   63 minutes

C   90 minutes

D   180 minutes

GO ON

38 Mr. Jones had his students line up for a drink of water. If Lee was 5th in line, which line-up shows Chris as 9th in line?

F

Lee Chris Jake Nan Dee

G

Lee Jake Chris Nan Dee

H

Lee Dee Jake Chris Nan

J

Lee Nan Jake Dee Chris

39 The hot-dog eating champion gobbled 152 hot dogs in one day. What is 152 rounded to the nearest hundred?

A 100

B 150

C 160

D 200

40 Mrs. Kroll's class voted for their favorite sport.

Favorite Sport

Sport	Number of Votes
Soccer	☆ ☆ ☆ ☆ ☆
Baseball	☆ ☆ ☆
Basketball	☆ ☆ ☆ ☆

KEY ☆ = 2 votes.

Which of the following statements about the pictograph is true?

F One more student voted for basketball than baseball.

G Two more students voted for soccer than baseball.

H One more student voted for soccer than basketball.

J Two more students voted for basketball than baseball.

41 Which of the shapes below is congruent to the shaded triangle?

A

B

C

D

42 Sandra is designing a game where players roll a cube. She plans to draw a different shape on each side of the cube.

How many shapes will she need to draw?

F 10

G 8

H 6

J 4

43 On a field trip to Roanoke, Mr. Diamond's class counted 358 Virginia license plates. On a field trip to Virginia Beach, Miss Lee's class counted 415 Virginia license plates. How many Virginia license plates did they count in all?

A 655

B 773

C 788

D 803

GO ON

44 Each day Diana wrote the number of minutes she spent doing homework on the note card shown.

Number of Minutes Spent Doing Homework		
10	15	20
30	10	20
30	15	25
30	20	30
35	25	

She started a line plot to show the data.

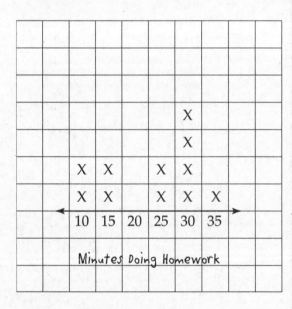

How many Xs should she put above the number 20?

F 6

G 5

H 4

J 3

45 Keith has an assortment of stamps. Some of his stamps have prairie dogs and some have spaceships. He wants to add the fraction of his stamps that have prairie dogs to the fraction of the stamps that have spaceships.

He added $\frac{2}{9} + \frac{4}{9}$ to get his answer.

What answer should Keith get?

A $\frac{5}{9}$

B $\frac{6}{9}$

C $\frac{7}{9}$

D $\frac{8}{9}$

GO ON

46 What is the value of the underlined 2 in 2̲89,657?

    F 20

    G 200

    H 2,000

    J 200,000

47 Which is a true number sentence?

    A $9 - 2 = 11 - 5$

    B $8 - 2 = 4 - 3$

    C $9 - 4 = 11 - 6$

    D $12 - 6 = 9 - 5$

48 Look at the fraction models.

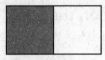

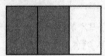

Which statement is true?

    F $\dfrac{1}{2} = \dfrac{2}{3}$

    G $\dfrac{1}{2} < \dfrac{2}{3}$

    H $\dfrac{2}{3} < \dfrac{1}{2}$

    J $\dfrac{1}{2} > \dfrac{2}{3}$

GO ON

49 Skyler surveyed his friends to determine the letter that is most liked by them. Each friend wrote his or her favorite letter on a card.

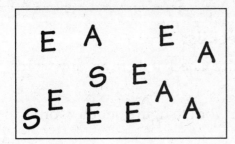

Which graph shows the correct number for each letter?

A
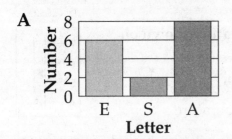

B
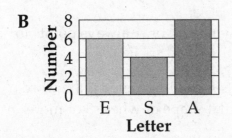

C
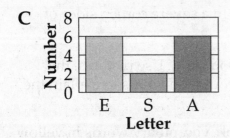

D
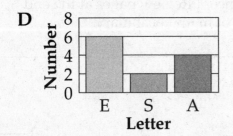

50 Which figure continues the pattern?

F ◯

G ▭

H △

J ▢

STOP

Key Vocabulary for SOL Assessment Success

Knowing what words and symbols mean can help you be successful
on the SOL Assessment. Use the vocabulary checklist to help you
figure out the meanings of words and symbols.

Key Vocabulary Checklist

☐ Always read directions and test items carefully. Check if there are any words
you don't know.

☐ Sometimes you can use part of the unknown word to figure out the word's
meaning.

> *Examples:* The word *rectangular* means "shaped like a rectangle."
> In a mixed number, a whole number is mixed with a fraction.

☐ Sometimes pictures or words before and after the unknown word give clues
about the word's meaning.

> *Example:* **Which is closest to the temperature shown on
> the thermometer?**
>
> The picture and the question above tell you that a
> thermometer is a tool that measures temperature.

☐ Sometimes you can make up something to help you remember the meanings
of words and symbols.

> *Examples:* The open, greater part of the symbol < or > always points to
> the greater number.
>
> A corner is a place where 2 or more streets meet. In geometry, the word
> *corner* is where 2 or more sides meet in a flat shape or where 3 or more
> edges meet in a solid figure.
>
> A square is a shape that has right angles. In a square corner, sides or
> edges meet to form right angles.

☐ Keep a vocabulary notebook of math words you learn. Use pictures, the
glossary at the back of your math book, and your own words to explain the
meanings of new math vocabulary.

☐ Before a test, review your vocabulary notebook, vocabulary words in yellow
in math lessons, and Key Vocabulary and Concept Review pages at the end
of each chapter to check your understanding of math vocabulary.

GO ON

Key Vocabulary for SOL Assessment Success *(continued)*

The SOL Assessment may use **symbols** instead of words to compare two whole numbers or fractions. The symbols >, <, and = are used to compare numbers. **>** means "is greater than." **<** means "is less than." **=** means " is equal to." A statement is **true** when the symbol shown correctly compares the two numbers.

SAMPLE	What You Think:
Which is true?	Look at **A**. Is it **true** that 7,384 is less than 5,658?
	Compare the thousands in **A**.
A 7,384 < 5,658	7 thousands is greater than 5 thousands, not less than. So, **A** is not true.
B 5,651 < 5,397	In **B**, the thousands are the same, so look at the hundreds.
C 7,123 < 7,849	6 hundreds is greater than 3 hundreds, so **B** is not true.
D 7,950 < 7,150	Compare the hundreds in **C**.
	1 hundred is less than 8 hundreds, so 7,123 is less than 7,849.
	The correct answer is **C**.

DIRECTIONS

Read and solve each question. Then mark the best answer. Use the information above and the checklist on page 200 for help.

1 Which is true?

    A 2,099 > 3,008

    B 9,487 > 9,291

    C 8,745 > 8,751

    D 3,200 > 3,555

2 Each figure below is shaded to represent a fraction. Which pair of figures makes a statement that is true?

    F ⬤ > ◗

    G ◗ > ✳

    H ◕ > ⬤

    J ✳ > ◔

3 Which symbol goes in the box to make the statement true?

    5,998 ☐ 6,750

    A <   **C** =

    B >   **D** +

4 Each figure below is shaded to represent a fraction. Which pair of figures makes a statement that is true?

    F ▮▮▮ < ▮▦

    G ▮☐☐ < ▦

    H ▮☐☐ < ▦

    J ▮▮☐ < ▦

© Pearson Education, Inc. 3

Key Vocabulary for SOL Assessment Success **201**

Problems Often Missed on Math Tests

Geometry problems are often missed on math tests. Some questions may ask about a shape or solid but not show a picture of it. Other questions may ask you to use pictures to identify or describe shapes or solids.

Geometry Checklist

☐ Make a sketch or picture the shape or solid in your mind.

☐ Think about what you know about the shape or solid.

☐ When you count faces (flat surfaces) on a solid, don't forget to count faces on the back, sides, and bottom of the figure.

☐ When you see outlines of shapes or solids, think of objects at home or in school that look like the picture.

Example:

a rectangular   looks   a shoe   **or**   a cereal
prism   like   box   box

☐ When you write about a shape or solid, use geometry words that best describe it.

SAMPLE

Which could be a face on a cone?

A △

B ⬠

C ◯

D ☐

What You Draw and Think:

A cone is a solid figure that is shaped like a sugar cone or an orange construction cone.

face →

There is only one face on a cone and it is shaped like a circle. So, the correct answer is **C**.

GO ON

DIRECTIONS
Read and solve each question. Then mark the best answer. Use the checklist on page 202 for help.

1 Which is a model of a sphere?

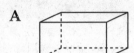

A

B

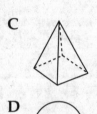

C

D

2 Tom drew a figure with 4 square corners. Which could be the figure he drew?

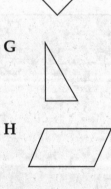

F

G

H

J

3 Ana is thinking of a shape with 3 sides. Which shape is she thinking of?

A Circle
B Triangle
C Square
D Rectangle

4 How many faces does a cube have?

F 8
G 6
H 5
J 4

5 Which of the following is shaped most like a cylinder?

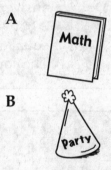

A

B

C

D

Math Rules for Better SOL Assessment Scores

Use these rules to help you remember multiplication facts. They can also help you eliminate incorrect answer choices.

Multiplication Rules

0: Any number multiplied by 0 is 0.
1: Any number multiplied by 1 is that number.
2: Any number multiplied by 2 will be an even number (will end in 0, 2, 4, 6, or 8).
5: Any number multiplied by 5 will end in 0 or 5.
9: When 1–10 are multiplied by 9, the digits of each product add up to 9.

SAMPLE 1	SAMPLE 2	SAMPLE 3
$4 \times 0 =$	$2 \times 3 =$	$5 \times 5 =$
A 40	**F** 2	**A** 25
B 4	**G** 3	**B** 24
C 1	**H** 6	**C** 16
D 0	**J** 7	**D** 10
What You Think: Any number multiplied by 0 is 0. So, $4 \times 0 = 0$. The correct answer is **D**.	**What You Think:** A number multiplied by 2 will be even, so the answer is not 3 or 7. $2 \times 1 = 2$, so 2×3 must equal 6. The correct answer is **H**.	**What You Think:** A number multiplied by 5 will end in 0 or 5, so the answer is not 24 or 16. $2 \times 5 = 10$, so 5×5 must equal 25. The correct answer is **A**.

SAMPLE 4	SAMPLE 5
$1 \times 7 =$	$8 \times 9 =$
F 0 **H** 7 **G** 1 **J** 8	**A** 73 **C** 64 **B** 72 **D** 17
What You Think: Any number multiplied by 1 is that number. So, $1 \times 7 = 7$. The correct answer is **H**.	**What You Think:** A number multiplied by 9 will have a product with digits that add up to 9. The only answer choice with digits that add up to 9 is 72 ($7 + 2 = 9$). The correct answer is **B**.

© Pearson Education, Inc. 3

DIRECTIONS

Read and solve each question. Then mark the best answer. Use the multiplication rules on page 204 for help.

1 $5 \times 6 =$

A 15
B 24
C 30
D 36

2 $9 \times 1 =$

F 10
G 9
H 8
J 1

3 Eric gave 3 stickers to each of 5 friends. How many stickers did he give away in all?

A 8
B 15
C 18
D 35

4 $2 \times 7 =$

F 5
G 9
H 13
J 14

5 There are 9 tables at a small restaurant. There is a vase with 4 flowers on each table. How many flowers are there in all?

A 13
B 35
C 36
D 144

6 $3 \times 0 =$

F 0
G 1
H 3
J 4

7 Carlos bought 4 packages of markers. There were 5 markers in each package. How many markers did he buy in all?

A 24
B 20
C 16
D 9

8 $7 \times 9 =$

F 79
G 63
H 56
J 16

9 Jane placed 1 stamp on each of 8 envelopes. How many stamps did she use altogether?

A 1
B 8
C 9
D 10

10 $6 \times 2 =$

F 8
G 9
H 12
J 13